LIKE IT IS TODAY: Paraphrased Parables

Like it is tODay

Paraphrased Parables

RICHARD MILHAM

BROADMAN PRESS
Nashville, Tennessee

Dewey Decimal Classification Number: 248.4
Library of Congress Catalog Card Number: 75–128858
Printed in the United States of America
21.5S70KSP

To

Julee

my darling

and disarming daughter

my constant source

of joy

Editor's Preface

This is an unusual book. It requires an explanation to you, the reader. Although you may read the book without such an explanation, for the book is a soundly Christian one, perfectly safe, and the devotional intent of the book is readily apparent upon completed reading, this explanation should dispel the question that will immediately come to your mind when you turn to the first page of text.

Broadman Press asked the author to write this book because parables of Jesus are completely timeless. Their message is relevant to any day and time. Yet, it seems to some of us, our own age needs to turn to these eternal verities from our Lord to a greater degree than any other modern era. It would be very simple to say, "Go read the Bible." Like all simple things, this is still the best and most effective way to guide a person to truth. Too often, however, men keep the diamonds of God's truth locked in a religious vault while they look upon secular rhinestones. So, Broadman Press asked the author to bring the diamonds of the parables out into a secular setting, to paraphrase the parables and certain similar passages into the language of our day.

This is an extremely difficult thing to do. Not only does it require a person of great Christian depth plus superior writing skill, in this case it requires a person with a passionate zeal to right the wrongs of our world, to return to the days when men's hearts were on fire for the Lord. We commend to you the author as a person having such qualifications.

But, there remains a problem.

It is impossible to paraphrase the parables of Jesus without having Jesus present as a character in such paraphrases. We feel that, for material this close to biblical, this we cannot do, the modern "scene" being what it is; presenting Jesus thus could be considered by some as irreverent. This is not quite the same situation as Dr. R. G. Lee's incomparably vivid language in the sermon "Payday Some Day." However, just as the flamboyant language of that epochal sermon intrigued many thousands to turn to the soberer words of the Scriptures and read there God's eternal laws of justice and retribution, even so does this book attempt to have the words and actions of "actors" lead you to the eternal words of the Lord.

So this book uses the technique of the Japanese *Kabuki* theatre rather than that of the early motion pictures. In early films (in the years before irreverence completely overtook our culture), the camera never showed the face of Jesus, only the back of an actor's head. The titles on the screen, though, or the words on the sound track, usually were the real words of Jesus, often as biblical quotations. Because of the culture in which we presently live, this book avoids even that; all the speeches in the following paraphrases are actors' speeches. As in the *Kabuki,* nothing in the following pages is "real"; neither the author nor the publishers would want you to listen unreservedly to *that man;* instead, we would point you to the Man from Galilee. Scripture verses are placed conveniently for this purpose.

WILLIAM CANNON
Editor, Inspirational Books
BROADMAN PRESS

Contents

Who Lives Next Door?

Luke 10:25–37

That man found himself in the middle again—which wasn't unusual. In fact it had become almost a way of life for him. This time he was locked up with a young lawyer who was probing him on a very personal level.

"Okay," the lawyer said, "for an hour now we've batted this religion bit around. Now let me tell you what really gives me a problem."

The young lawyer took his time, wanting to phrase the question in just the right terms.

"What is it that is expected of a fellow like myself in order to be assured of this everlasting life you're always holding out?"

A smile flashed across the face of *that man.*

"Bill, you've got a good mind. In the light of everything we've discussed, what kind of answer do you think I'd give?"

The young lawyer pondered for a long moment, obviously caught up in the challenge.

"Okay," he finally sighed, "I'll give it a try. I believe that this thing starts with a complete sell out of our selves to God. We have to love Him with everything we've got—our hearts, our minds, all our strength—every fiber of whatever it is that makes us individual human beings."

That man nodded his head approvingly and indicated for the young lawyer to continue.

". . . and then, out of that experience with God, we should

live the kind of lives that makes us love our neighbor and want
to help him. We have to learn to love him as much as we love
and care for our own lives."

"You're to be congratulated, Bill," *that man* stated warmly.
"You are not far from dead center."

But Bill wasn't through yet. Even though he had given an
answer, his lawyer mind flashed a warning signal. There was a
piece missing somewhere in the discussion. It was only a moment before he located it and excitedly blurted out:

"Yes, but who is my neighbor?"

"Okay, Bill," *that man* responded, "let's get practical at that
point. Instead of debating the question, let me tell you a story.
You see if it makes sense."

Bill nodded for him to go ahead and settled back to analyze
his words as carefully as possible.

The owner of a men's clothing store closed up his shop
early one afternoon and decided to take a walk through a
nearby park on his way home.

Unfortunately he was attacked by some young addicts
who were getting desperate for some money to carry on
their habit.

He was brutally beaten with a piece of pipe and kicked
viciously until he finally lost consciousness. The man was
robbed, stripped of his clothes, and left for dead.

Later, when the man regained consciousness, he managed, in spite of his severe pain, to drag himself to the entrance of the park and there fell unconscious once again.

At that particular corner there was a street light. In a

moment, a car pulled up and stopped for the red signal. The man in the car happened to glance over toward the park and was shocked to see the near naked figure lying there bleeding on the cement walk.

"Somebody ought to do something about that," he muttered to himself. "Sights like that will tend to ruin the image of our city."

He grew impatient for the light to change. Hesitantly, he glanced a second time at the battered form.

"I guess somebody has reported him by this time. Those police ought to hurry and get him off the street. That's what we pay them for."

The light changed. The man sped off, glad to be out of sight and sound of that nauseating spectacle.

He got his mind back on his destination now and, checking his watch, was glad to see he'd be able to make it on time.

"I'm glad I won't miss that deacons' meeting," he muttered to himself, ". . . I sure hope I don't get any static on my proposal to send those medical supplies to our missionaries in Tanzania. God knows how much those people need help."

He said it with what could be called "genuine concern."

■ ■ ■

It was only a moment before another car came to stop at that traffic light. The two ministers in the car were deeply engrossed in a theological debate when one of them happened to glance in the direction of the still bleeding form.

"Henry," he blurted excitedly, "would you look at that!"

The second minister strained his neck around to get a good look at the scene.

"How many times, Henry—how many times—do you have to warn people before they find out what booze will do to them?"

The good minister shook his head in wonderment.

"Look at that, will you. Now if that isn't a good sermon illustration I've never seen one. In fact, I think I'll use it this Sunday while it's still fresh in my mind."

The battered man happened to take that particular moment to try to get to his feet, but the pain seared through him, and he crumbled to the pavement again.

"Look, Henry," the good minister exploded again, "what an idiot that man is making of himself."

Henry nodded his head in agreement. He just couldn't understand why people would get themselves into that condition when the Christian life was such a wonderful, warm adventure of living.

The light changed, the car sped off, and the battered man was soon forgotten as the conversation took another direction.

"Henry, I'm sure glad we started taking this pastoral counseling course we're headed for at the hospital."

The other minister again nodded his head in agreement.

"You know," the first minister said with compassion, "I never realized how much misery there is in the world—and I feel myself becoming more sensitive to people's needs every day."

He sighed with deep satisfaction.

"You know, Henry, that this afternoon's session is going to teach us how to recognize people in need."

■ ■ ■

The man at the gate was beginning to feel the pain more intensely now. It seared through his lungs and stabbed into every muscle.

In the agony of that moment he suddenly felt a soft touch on his face and opening his eyes looked into the bearded face of a weirdly spectacled, barefoot young man.

"Man, you really got worked over," the young man said with real concern. "We got to get you some help."

He peeled off his shirt and draped it over the man's shoulders. Taking his bandana, he gently wiped the perspiration from the blood-smeared face.

Although the injured man was considerably larger, the young man got his weight on his shoulders and helped him to his feet.

The weakened man started to slip to the ground again.

"Don't go out on me now, man," the young man encouraged him. "We'll make it. Only about three blocks to a hospital, man. We'll make it."

And make it they did, although every step was torturing.

Once in the emergency ward of the hospital, the young man gently eased the battered body into a chair and dashed to the admittance desk.

"Man, you got to hurry," he gasped tiredly, "this cat is in bad shape—he's hurt bad."

The receptionist looked at him. A frown crossed her face as she noticed the bare feet and long hair.

"You'll have to fill out some insurance forms," she finally said coldly.

"Insurance forms!" the young man exploded. "Look, I got a hurt man bleeding out there . . . how about some help!"

"I'm sorry about that," she fired back, "but who is going to pay the bill?"

"How do I know!" the young man exploded for a second time, "I don't even know his name . . ."

"I'm sorry, but somebody has got to . . ."

"Listen woman, whatever I got you can have, and if I don't have enough bread, I'll get it! I'll sign anything you want, and I'll pay any bill he rings up, but you get that man some help—and you get it now!"

That man finished and stared at the young lawyer.

"Now Bill, in your opinion, which of these three demonstrated what the word neighbor really means?"

Bill sighed, still reflecting on the story:

"The one who showed concern in his actions."

"Right, Bill. Now why don't you try a little of that practical living and concern-showing and not just be academic about it?"

A Surgeon's Search

John 3:1–18 (non-parable)

For some time now Nick had been contemplating the possibility. He and his colleagues had been arguing for days over whether this one they called *that man* was the genuine article or just another religious fraud. Nick had decided to find out for himself. The decision didn't come easy for him. Not many hard-nosed, no-nonsense surgeons purposely get themselves involved in a religious debate, but Nick had made up his mind, and he was going to see the matter through.

Nick set up an appointment. Late one night, after an especially hard day at the hospital, he found himself at *that man's* apartment. He was a little surprised at how congenially he was received by the man who had only been a rumor to him up to this time. *That man* poured a couple of cups of coffee, and both men settled back into their chairs to get down to business.

"One of the reasons I'm here," Nick explained, "is because many of us have been impressed with the things that have been reported about you."

"What kind of things, Nick?"

"Well, you know. For instance, the healings that have been credited to some kind of power you are supposed to possess. Now I'm not saying that some don't have their doubts, but the evidence is pretty impressive."

Nick paused for a moment to take a long gulp of his coffee. "We surgeons know the limitations of our skill, but, if the reports are correct, only God himself could give a man your kind of power and ability. I guess that's really what I've come to find out—whether it is possible that God could actually reign in a man's life with that kind of certainty."

"Let's get to it, Nick. You didn't come here to butter me up with compliments. You came looking to find out if God can become a living reality within your own life."

It was evident that he had put his finger on the real issue. Nick stared at him intently and nodded for him to go on.

"Okay, Nick, I'm going to tell it to you as straight as I know how. You don't have a chance of encountering a living God or experiencing his reign and rule within your life without undergoing some radical surgery in your makeup. Nick, it's surgery that's so radical that it's as revolutionary as if a man were born all over again."

Nick was obviously stunned by these remarks. He was prepared to hear a recital of some religious formula, or listen to a discourse on the nature of God, but this man was telling him something radically different.

"What are you talking about?" Nick finally exploded. "Don't you know you are talking to one of the best surgeons around? Don't try to tell me about medicine, and don't try to wise off about being born again! In all my years in the medical profession, I've never seen a man crawl back into his mother's womb and be born a second time. What you are talking about is physically impossible."

"Come on, Nick. Use your head. You've been in a shell too long. Wake up! I'm talking about spiritual realities. I'm talking about the kind of stuff you can't find with your scalpel or under your microscope. Listen, Nick, I'm going to give it to you straight a second time. Unless you experience a radical transformation of your nature, you cannot know the reign of God upon you and in you."

Nick was becoming thoroughly perplexed. He was well acquainted with every religious system in practice, but this man was pressing him for some kind of personal experience.

"Sure, Nick, you know all about the mechanics of physical birth and maternity wards, but you don't know a thing about spiritual birth or God-realities."

That man paused for a moment and looked intently at Nick. "Don't be so surprised, Nick, when I tell you that you must be prepared before you can enter into this arena of life."

"Okay," Nick countered, "you keep talking about these so-called spiritual realities; but how do I even know they exist? I deal with a world I can see and test, and you keep insisting that I discover some kind of intangible reality. I can't accept it."

"Who are you kidding, Nick?" *that man* fired back. "Your whole life is filled with realities you can't touch or measure. Can you dissect the love that you have for your children? Can you bottle up and sell the concern that shines in the eyes of an expectant mother? Have you ever held an electron in the palm of your hand?"

Nick didn't answer. Instead he rose to his feet and started pacing across the floor.

"Wake up, Nick," *that man* continued, "God is real and can be experienced. Nick, you know how the wind rushes in and caresses us and then moves on. We can't see it with our physical eye, yet we feel and experience its reality as it touches us. Nick, that's just like a man who experiences the personal touch of God upon his life—the evidence is in the experience, in the changed life, in the overwhelming assurance that God is real within us."

Nick was still pacing, but it was evident that he was in deep thought. He stopped and turned directly to catch *that man's* eye and with a certain longing in his voice asked, "Okay, you say it can happen, but, tell me—how can it happen in my life?"

"You're probably one of the most learned men in this city, Nick, and you're no beginner in knowing your Bible either, but you have really missed the heart of it all because you haven't taken a really good hard look at me."

"What do you mean?" Nick replied curiously. "I'm here, am I not? And I've been pretty fair in my remarks about you."

"Oh, yes, Nick," *that man* replied quietly, "you were kind enough to compliment me by some insinuation that God might really be working in me, but take another look—a real long look —because I'm going to tell you something that will challenge every fiber of faith you possess."

The two men stared at each other. The silence of the moment was intense.

"Nick, you are looking at the one that God has sent to make that experience possible for you and for every man who will come to accept me."

"You mean that, don't you?" gasped Nick. "You really feel that God has sent you!"

"Not feel, Nick, know. I'm not giving you some pie-in-the-sky religious fantasy, I'm trying to tell you that God is actually present in our midst—right now."

Nick was still stunned by the implications of the man's remarks but gathered his thoughts enough to mutter:

"But, how, how are you going to do it? How are you going to make it possible for men like me to find God as a living reality?"

"Through death, Nick. I'm going to do it through a death that will bring life."

That man walked over to the apartment window and looked out over the swimming pool crowded with bathers.

"Nick, do you remember an Old Testament account about Moses and the children of Israel? He was leading them through a desert wilderness to the land God had promised when they were overwhelmed by deadly snakes."

Nick nodded his head, indicating he was familiar with the incident.

"Well, you remember then that God told Moses to make a snake of bronze and lift it high on the end of a pole; and those that were bitten were told that if they would look at the bronze snake, they would live."

"I remember," Nick responded quietly.

That man walked away from the window and came over to where Nick stood. He looked him squarely in the eye.

"Nick, you may not understand this now, but the lifting up of God's Son like that snake challenges dying men to look to Him as the giver of life."

For the first time in some time, *that man* smiled.

"You see, Nick, this God that you are seeking to know really loves you and every man. In fact, he loves you so much that he has packaged up a gift for you—a gift of life—abundant life—life that begins now and goes on into endless tomorrows; and, Nick, God has sent his Son to deliver it."

Nick stared deeply into *that man's* face and wondered if it all could be so.

"You see, Nick, God didn't send his Son into this world to damn it but to save it and give it meaning. As I said, you may not understand it all now, but before very long you will."

A Promoter's Proposition

Matt. 4:1–11 (non-parable)

"I've been watching you closely for these past months, and I think you've got what it takes to make real headlines."

That man sat silently, rubbing his weary eyes as the little man kept up his fast-paced chatter.

"With that smooth love bit you preach and those fantastic healing bits, you can't fail. All you need is a little publicity."

The little man smiled gleefully.

"With me as your promoter we can clean up!"

That man still made no reply but merely rubbed the back of his neck, trying to relieve some of the accumulated tension.

"Listen, I know all about your religious kick. If you want to say God does things through you, okay. That will make great publicity, but remember I'll be calling all the shots."

For the first time *that man* took a good long look at the one making the proposition. The little man certainly looked successful—expensive shoes, elegant suit, razor hair cut. In fact, he fairly gleamed with confidence.

That man felt the stubble of his beard. For days now he had been under tremendous pressure, trying to clarify the direction his life should take in God's service. He was tired, and he was hungry, and, now, to top it off, he was being forced to face this smooth talking promoter with his big promises of fame and fortune.

"I don't understand you, man," the promoter piped up. "You really look famished. Why don't you take a few of these acorns and turn them into TV dinners?"

The promoter smiled ever so slyly.

"That way we can kill two birds with one stone—you could grab a bite to eat, and I could catch your act firsthand and see if you really live up to this God bit."

A bit of a smile flashed across *that man's* face.

"Your values are really something," he asserted, breaking his silence for the first time. "You think that a man serves God in order to be assured a meal ticket?"

The promoter was caught a little off balance by this unexpected challenge.

"Listen," *that man* continued, "a person discovers what it means to really live not in terms of just filling his stomach but in discovering that he belongs to a living God who wants every dimension of his life."

The promoter was getting a little nervous, but *that man* wasn't finished with him yet.

"Living is not just staying alive like an animal. Living is coming to find out that you are the special object of God's love and concern. That's what makes life worth the living."

"Okay, okay," the little man muttered, "I didn't mean to get you so riled up. I just thought it would be a good chance to see you in action. If you don't want to do it, forget it."

There was a moment of silence. Suddenly, though, with a snap of his fingers, the promoter blurted out.

"I've got it! I know just the thing!"

The promoter led him to an expensive sports car. Soon they were screeching to a halt in front of a massive cathedral.

"Now here's what I'd like to suggest. In about an hour

there's going to be a service here. This place will be packed with hundreds of people."

Excitement was showing in the promoter's voice now as he saw the whole plot unraveling before his eyes.

"Well, about halfway through the service I want you to jump from the balcony down to the altar."

The promoter was gesturing dramatically with his hands.

"You know the bit—kinda float down."

A sudden inspiration lit his eyes.

"Wait! Better yet, with that God-bit, you could hustle up a couple of angels, and each one could hold on to an arm. Man, that would be sensational!"

The little man turned to him with a dramatic flourish.

"Well, what do you say?"

That man was obviously becoming more exhausted. He was feeling even more deeply the pangs of hunger, but, in spite of this, his eyes fairly flashed as he replied.

"You still don't see it, do you? You think that God's presence in the lives of men who yield to him is some kind of gimmick to be manipulated?"

Again the little man was not prepared for such a response.

"God is not to be toyed with. He doesn't enter as King of a man's life and claim him as a subject only to have the subject start giving orders and playing with divine power."

"Okay, okay, relax. I'm sorry I got you upset."

The promoter was staring at him intently now.

"Okay, I'm going to level with you. I knew that you were having a rough time, so I figured I could step in, offer you a few quick bucks, and make a killing off your act; but you got class."

The promoter paused for a moment to let the big announcement hit with a dramatic flair.

"Because you got class and real talent, I'm going to offer you a partnerhip. Now listen, I'm no small-time operator. I own this town and all the action. All I want you to do in return is turn over that talent of yours into my hands, and, all I got, you got. No man in his right mind would turn that down."

The promoter reached into his coat pocket and pulled out a folded piece of paper.

"This is a solid contract that will tie us up for life. Here's my pen. Just sign on the bottom line."

That man stared at the paper for a moment and then exploded.

"Become a partner with you? What kind of a fool do you take me for? Any man that does business with you would have to sell out his soul!"

The eyes of the promoter started to fill with fire. But *that man* continued:

"Let me tell you something, little man! I've already got a partnership—a partnership with a God I love and serve; and no man is going to buy me off. You might as well be moving on because you just struck out completely."

The smile and suaveness were gone now. The promoter's face was contorted with the hate that had hidden behind it for so long. He reached into his pocket, pulled out a cigarette lighter, and set the contract on fire.

"Okay," he snarled, "so you don't want to play ball with me! But I guarantee you it's not over yet. The hour will come when we will meet again."

That man stared at the contract as it burned into ashes. When he finally looked up, the little man had strangely vanished.

Congratulations

Matt. 5:1–12 (non-parable)

Blessed are the poor in spirit: for theirs is the kingdom of heaven. (To be congratulated is the man who comes to realize that he is absolutely destitute without God and comes to trust Him completely, for of such who offer unreserved obedience to God is made up God's sovereign reign and witness among men.)

Blessed are they that mourn: for they shall be comforted. (To be congratulated is the man who discovers that in his sorrow and pain, in his concern and care for others, and in his struggle with his own sin—there is found the presence and power of a healing God.)

Blessed are the meek: for they shall inherit the earth. (To be congratulated is the man who knows how to control his anger and yet can be stirred to constructive action; who has learned to bring under discipline all his potential for God and is marked by a spirit that realized his limitations and need of God; for that kind of man will be master over men.)

Blessed are they which do hunger and thirst after righteousness: for they shall be filled. (To be congratulated is the man who yearns for a right relationship with God, as a strong man seeks food, and a thirsty man desires water, for that man will discover complete satisfaction.)

Blessed are the merciful: for they shall obtain mercy. (To be congratulated is the man who has the sensitivity to get inside the skin of another human being and feel what he feels, think what he thinks, hurt as he hurts; for he will be better prepared to forgive others and thereby come to experience what God's forgiveness in Christ is really like.)

Blessed are the pure in heart: for they shall see God. (To be congratulated is the man who acts out of pure motives—who seeks to serve God not for self-esteem and men's praise but who desires his Lord to be lifted up, for such a man senses God's presence in everything and everyone around him.)

Blessed are the peacemakers: for they shall be called the children of God. (To be congratulated is the man who loves the peace that God has given him, and who takes that peace into the arena of life—offering it as a bridge between God and man in reconciliation, and between man and man in society; for such a man is doing a Godlike work.)

Blessed are they which are persecuted for righteousness' sake: for theirs is the kingdom of heaven. Blessed are ye, when men shall revile you, and persecute you, and shall say all manner of evil against you falsely, for my sake. Rejoice and be exceeding glad: for great is your reward in heaven: for so persecuted the prophets which were before you. (To be congratulated is the man who encounters resistance toward his Christian commitments, for he has the rare privilege of experiencing to a small degree the sufferings of his Lord that brought him redemption. That man ought to leap with joy, for through these experiences he can learn to a greater degree the sense of God's reign within his life. It is also of interest to note that, in suffering, a man finds himself in pretty good company.)

The Healing Touch

Matt. 5:13

You are like antibiotics to a sick world; but, if the medicine has lost its potency, what good is it, except to be thrown away?

A Blessed Beacon

Matt. 5:14

You are like a towering lighthouse set on the rocks to show men the way to safety.

A Matter of Pride

Matt. 5:15

No one buys a new car and then hides it in the garage, but parks it out front so all can see and admire it.

A Foolish Spirit

Matt. 6:25–34

Why pray when you can worry?

A Prescription For Prayer

Matt. 7:7–11 & Luke 11:5–13

"I just don't know how I ought to pray," the troubled man said sincerely. "I don't know if God is really answering me."

That man understood the honest probing that was reflected in the man's words.

"Okay, Jim, I can easily see how you could have a problem at this point, but maybe you are making it more difficult for yourself than it really is."

The troubled man looked intently at him.

"I can't handle all of the problem right now, Jim," *that man* continued, "but let me give you a few directions about what ought to be your attitude in praying and what you can expect from God in the way of a response."

"I can certainly use all the help I can get," the troubled man responded, "but I'm not much of a religious man. I don't know if I can understand a lot of religious talk."

"Relax, Jim," *that man* replied, smiling. "I'm not going to preach to you, I'm just going to tell you a story."

A fine father awoke one night to find that his child was very sick and was running a dangerously high fever. He called his doctor and was told that a certain medication had to be obtained and administered immediately.

Since it was late at night, the father discovered, on ar-riving, that the drugstore had been closed. He rushed immediately to the home of the pharmacist, who was also a good friend, and started ringing the doorbell.

"Hey, Stan, get up, will you!" he shouted up toward the bedroom window. "I've got a sick child and I need a prescription filled now!"

The pharmacist was naturally awakened by the com-motion and opening his window whispered, "Hey, Ned, keep it down out there. What are you trying to do, wake up the neighborhood?"

"I'm sorry, Stan," the worried father responded, "but you got to get down here and open the store now—there's no time to lose."

"Come on, Ned, why bother me this time of night," the pharmacist said with a little irritation. "My family's all asleep. I'm in my pajamas, and I just don't feel like get-ting dressed. Come on by in the morning. Nothing could be that important that it won't keep the night."

"I'm not kidding, Stan!" The frantic father was yelling now. "I've got to have that medicine tonight!"

"Hey, quiet down, Ned," the pharmacist pleaded. "You'll wake my family up."

"Listen, Stan, I'll make it as clear as I know how. I'm going to stay right here and pound on your door and yell at your window until I get what I came for!"

"Okay, okay, Ned," the pharmacist replied with exas-peration, "I'll be down in just a moment."

As he headed for the closet to get his clothes out, he muttered to himself, "I've never seen anyone so persist-ent."

When Stan finally got out to Ned's car, Ned couldn't

resist asking him, "Stan, would you really have turned me away?"

"Nah, Ned," he said with a smile, "I just wanted to see how desperately you really needed that medicine."

That man was interrupted at this point in the story.

"I get it," Jim blurted out excitedly, "all I have to do is really be sincere and persistent with God when I pray to Him and He will give me anything I ask for."

"Hold on a minute, Jim," *that man* cautioned, "That's not all there is to the story. Let me finish it first before you jump to any conclusions."

Jim settled back and indicated that he was ready for *that man* to continue his narrative.

When Stan and Ned arrived at the drugstore, Ned started insisting that the particular medication Ned was preparing was not what the doctor ordered.

In fact Ned started to insist that Stan give him a particular drug that the pharmacist knew to be deadly.

"Stan, I'm sure that's what the doctor told me to get," he pressed, "and that's what I'm leaving here with."

"But, Ned," the pharmacist responded, "that stuff is poison. It could kill your child. It most certainly would make her seriously ill."

"You must be wrong, Stan," Ned continued to insist, "that's the medicine I want. I know that's what the doctor told me to get."

"Ned, I hate to pull rank on you, but I'm far better qualified to know what is good for your child and what will hurt her. You better trust my judgment to give you the right medicine even though you apparently feel you know what is best."

It took Ned only a moment to see the wisdom in Stan's position, and he quietly nodded for him to go ahead with the preparation of the prescription as he saw fit.

"Now, Jim," *that man* said, turning to the troubled man, "maybe you can see the total picture. From God's perspective, He knows what kinds of things are like poisons to our lives. Jim, he always answers our prayers, not just in terms of giving us what we ask for, but in terms of what is best for us."

Jim was beginning to put the pieces together now, and he started to feel a new assurance.

"Jim," *that man* continued, "God is just like a father who really loves his children and wants the best for them.

"Look at your life. Even though you are a finite, imperfect human being, you know how to love your children and desire only good things for them."

"You're right," Jim muttered, "I want only the best for my family."

"Okay, then, let me ask you. If your child came to you and asked you for a pet, would you give him a deadly snake?"

Jim's astonished look was all the reply he needed.

". . . or if he should ask you for a jelly sandwich, would you give him arsenic?"

"No, how in God's heaven could any man do that to a child he loves?"

"Right, Jim," he continued. "Have you ever considered how much more God loves us? We are his children, and he will never give us anything in our lives that would destroy us, even though from our limited viewpoint we think it is good for us."

"Then it's not just asking for things, is it?"

"No, Jim, it's asking, and then trusting God to respond in the way that will be for our very best."

A Narrow Target

Matt. 7:13–14

Many shots are taken at a soccer goal, but the one that counts is the one that hits the narrow target.

Beware

Matt. 7:15

Beware of a used car salesman who calls himself Honest John.

The Proper Smell

Matt. 7:16

You can't expect a skunk to give off a scent like Chanel #5.

Formal Religion

Matt. 7:21–23

Not everyone who recites the Apostles' Creed and has a perfect record of Sunday School attendance will enter into God's eternal reign, but only he who has a personal experience of God's grace.

The Two Pilots

Matt. 7:24–27

The man who hears the words of his Lord and obeys them is like the pilot who reinforces his aircraft so he can withstand the destructive forces of the elements.

The man who hears the words of the Lord and does not obey them is like a man who takes off in a flimsy aircraft into the teeth of a howling gale and is shattered to pieces.

Act I

Mark 10:17–22 (non-parable)

One moment *that man* was walking quietly down a shaded street, and the next moment he was startled by an automobile that swerved right in beside him at the curb. A smiling young man with disheveled hair popped his head out the window.

"Hey, I didn't mean to make you jump, but I've been trying to get up with you for days."

In a moment he had scrambled out of his car and come to face *that man* with excited anticipation. He didn't hesitate in coming right out with what had driven him to seek out this particular man.

"I've heard from some of my friends that you can give a fellow the straight on how to really find some meaning in life."

He paused for a moment, trying to read some kind of response in *that man's* face, but continued.

"I am really fed up with it—the whole rat race. I don't want much out of life—just a little peace and quiet."

That man still made no response but indicated for the young man to join him at a nearby bench.

"I've heard that you've been handing out some real claims— stuff like God being interested in our life, and even stuff like being able to have life after death."

The young man had grown intense now.

"I want a piece of that action," he exploded with deep emotion. "Whatever it costs—I'll buy it!"

That man finally broke his silence.

"Why do you come to me?" he began quietly. "Do you think that I am God? You must know that an ordinary man couldn't make such claims."

The young man was startled by this unusual question.

"Well, I don't know," he answered with all honesty. "I just heard you could deliver something to me that would give me a good reason for kicking around in this life."

The young man continued to probe his own reasons for coming to this place in his life.

". . . I guess I figured you could give me something—well something . . . religious."

"Well if it's something religious you want," *that man* responded, "why not obey the commandments? You know them: don't steal, don't kill—"

"Hold on there," the young man interrupted. "I might not look like it, but I cut my teeth on those commandments, and I figure I've done pretty good with them. I haven't killed anyone or stolen from people—"

This time *that man* interrupted.

"Okay, let's take it for granted that you've obeyed the commandments fairly well, but you tell me that you still are unable to find any real peace with yourself and, I imagine, with God also."

"You're right," the young man admitted, "that's why I'm here. I figure you can give me a new angle."

"Okay, if you're really serious and you truly desire to discover peace within your life, then I want you to do only one thing."

The young man became extremely curious now.

"What kind of thing?"

"There's only one thing really missing. You've got the form

of a religion that is doing you no good. Now all you need to do is discover a faith that can transform you."

"Okay, okay," the young man blurted out in exasperation, "but how do I find it—what do I have to do?"

It seemed like an eternity before *that man* finally answered. "Sell your car," he said quietly.

"What!" the young man exploded with a startled expression.

". . . and," *that man* continued firmly, "your home, your business."

"Wait a minute!" the young man protested again.

". . . all you have—sell it all and then give away every cent you have made."

"Now hold on there," the young man pleaded, "I didn't count on anything like this."

"But you do want real peace," *that man* reminded him, "and you did say you would pay any price."

"Yes, I know I did," he replied hesitantly, "but this whole thing is going a little too far."

"Then what you really mean," *that man* probed with tenderness, "is that in your life your wealth has first place."

"Well, I'm not sure I'd put it that way, but I'm sure not going to give it up. You don't know how much money you're talking about."

"Even if it meant finding what you have been searching for?" *that man* questioned.

"No, sir, I'm not going to give it up."

The young man started back for his car muttering, "I'm not going to give it up—not a cent of it!" He drove off.

Sadness flooded *that man*. In those few moments he had grown to love the young man and his enthusiastic strivings, but he had come to see again how easy it is to yearn for God, but how hard to yield him first place in one's life.

Act II

Luke 12:16–21

He was excited, extremely delighted, and relieved beyond measure. Six solid months of hard work had finally resulted in his being awarded the largest contract his manufacturing firm had ever received.

Like a child with a new toy, he went pacing around his plant making plans to expand his facilities in order to handle the large influx of business that was on the way.

"Hey, Ben," he shouted to his burly foreman, "come over here a minute."

Ben lumbered over to his boss, wiping his hands of accumulated grime.

"Boss, we've got to get a new gearbox for that crane. It's not going to hold out much longer."

"Don't worry about it, Ben," he said laughingly. "I'm going to buy you a new crane."

The boss relished the look of surprise that crossed his old friend's face.

"Ben, we got the Benson contract."

The burly foreman's eyes widened with excitement.

"No kidding," he blurted joyfully, "that's great. It's about time we cracked the big-time manufacturing."

"I know, Ben, and I'm not going to forget how you stuck with me during those early lean years."

This moment was not easy in coming. Although he had in-herited some wealth from his youth, he had decided that he could not be satisfied until he had amassed what he could con-sider a fortune.

From his youth, therefore, he poured every waking minute of his life into this dream. He fought and scraped—always driving himself toward that day when he could feel he had all the wealth that would satisfy him.

Naturally there was very little time for anything or anyone else. Little enough time for his wife and children, much less any time for God and church.

"But now," he thought to himself, "now I've finally got it made. Now I can relax, take a vacation, spend some time with my family. I've got all I need to last me the rest of my life."

That night at supper he fairly bubbled over with excitement.

"Honey, in a few months we're going to take off from this town and fly around the world. We're going to do all the things we've ever talked about."

His wife sat there, strangely silent. She had heard this begin-ning so many times before, but never had it really come to pass.

"I know what you're thinking, honey," he said, sensing her unbelief, "but it's going to be different this time. That contract set me up for life—no more worries."

She looked at him with a new tenderness. "Maybe this time," she thought prayerfully to herself, "it will be different."

"I mean it honey. Now we can make up for all those lost hours and start to live again."

It was during this meal that he felt a few pangs.

"Indigestion," he thought, "I'll have to slow down on my eat-ing."

After supper he did an unusual thing. He called his two boys aside and told them about the contract and how much he was looking forward to spending some time with them in the days ahead.

"In fact, fellows," he chimed happily, "I'll be at your ball game Thursday. I've heard it's going to be a big one. How's that for a start?"

They were surprised and even a little excited. They had made quite a reputation for themselves in baseball, but very few times had their father been around to share it with them.

". . . and you might as well plan to see a lot of me this summer," the father continued. "We'll start with a fishing trip."

Again he felt the sharp pains, but wrote it off to all the excitement of the day.

"This has been such a good day," he thought contentedly to himself, "I'm really going to start enjoying life."

Sleep was late in coming. His mind was reeling with plans for the future. He had just dozed off when the wave of pain swept over his body. His chest felt as though it would explode. He sat upright in his bed clutching his throat.

In that moment of agony he thought he heard a voice crying mournfully:

"Oh, how foolish . . . now that life is coming to an end! What have you done to prepare yourself for eternity?"

Sweat poured from his brow. His face was contorted in agony. Again the voice seemed to rip into his pain:

"Take one last look. See everything you've ever earned crumbling before your eyes. See everyone fighting over your possessions—those same possessions you killed yourself for—and be aware—be aware—that you have been so busy making a living that you have never lived."

The pain was beyond bearing now.

"Too late—too late now."

Act III

Luke 16:19–31

He had never felt such aloneness before.

"Where is my wife," he choked.

Only that awful echo: "Not here, your wife is not here."

He tried to piece it all together, but the darkness was too thick. Once in a while he thought he could see a blurred figure or hear an anguished moan.

He remembered the pain—those last moments of terror—but it was nothing compared to the feelings that were creeping into his awareness now. Again he cried:

"Where is my wife?"

"Your wife is not here."

"Where are my children?"

"Your children are not here."

He started to grope about in the darkness, but all was blindness.

"My God!" he howled again, "let me feel the presence of one single human being!"

"My God"—he hadn't said those words in such a long time— "My God"—and now they seemed so hollow.

Terror was welling up in him. He felt like a small child being threatened by deep darkness. No candle anywhere. No love anywhere. No voice anywhere.

"Where is my wife?" he screamed.

"Your wife is not here."

"Where are my children?" he pleaded.

"Your children are not here."

Then the greatest fear of all came to his mind. . . . He was terrified to ask but he knew he would have to. . . . His whole body trembled as he pursed his lips and wailed into that nebulous night:

"Where . . . oh, where is God!"

As the deepest of all darkness closed in on his soul for all eternity, he heard that hideous echo whispering that most horrifying of all judgments:

"God is not here."

For the Love of a Cat

Luke 15:1–7

An elderly woman who had been widowed for many years had come to find much companionship in her declining years with her collection of cats. Naturally she came to love each one of them as a mother loves each of her children.

One morning, as she was feeding them, she discovered to her dismay that one was missing. She waited until late afternoon, hoping that the cat would show up, but to no avail. Realizing that something serious must have happened to her cat, the elderly woman set out to find him.

She walked for several hours throughout the neighborhood until her strength gave out. Sadly she started for home when she was stopped by a gentle meow. Following the sound of the pitiful cry, she found her lost cat stuck between two trash cans in a side alley. Gently she freed him and hugged him ever so carefully and wearily returned home.

Though tired as she was, her excitement in finding her cat was too much to contain. She called a good neighbor and invited her over to have a little celebration.

"Martha, I found my precious cat. It was a long anxious day, but I have found my lost cat.

"Do you think I'm silly for caring that much over a little cat?" She paused for a moment, then answered her own question, "But I do I love them—every one of them."

Missing Her

Matt. 9:14–15

It doesn't make sense for a young man to waste his time missing his girl friend when she is sitting there beside him. He can spend his time pining over her tomorrow when she has returned to college.

Watch Out

Matt. 9:16–17

It is a dangerous thing to toss a cat into the middle of a dog kennel or to throw a lighted match into a keg of gunpowder.

A Joyful Moment

Luke 15:8–10

God seeks for us and rejoices in finding us in much the same way a woman rejoices when she finds her lost book of trading stamps.

Back from the Dead

Luke 15:11–32

"You must be kidding me, Allan!"

"No, Pop, I mean it. I want out!"

"But, Allan, use your head," the distraught father pleaded, trying to control his temper. "Only two more months and you will be out of high school. You'd be a fool to miss graduating."

"I don't care, Pop," the young man stormed back, "I've had it. I'm fed up with school—with people telling me what to do —the whole mess—and I want out. I want to be on my own!"

"I can't understand what has gotten into you," the father responded, shaking his head in bewilderment. "I know we've had some pretty strong arguments, and we don't see eye to eye on a lot of things, but I don't see why you would want to leave."

"Pop, I don't want to argue," the young man exploded in exasperation. "I just want out!"

"But, Allan, look at your brother. Bob graduated last year, and he's making it at college and seems plenty content. There's no reason you can't finish out high school, and then things might look a little different to you."

"Pop, please listen," the young man interrupted, "I don't care about Bob or what he did or is doing. For that matter, I don't care about anyone else right now. All I am interested in at this moment is number one."

The father could begin to sense how useless his arguments were, and so he just sat quietly.

"Now I want out," the young man continued, "and I'm getting out. You can't stop me. If you don't want to help give me a send-off, okay, I'll just cut out completely on my own."

His father stared at him trying to understand, trying to comprehend what was driving his son with such intensity.

"You really mean that, don't you, Allan?"

"Yes, I do, Pop. I really mean it. As much as I've ever meant anything in my life."

"Allan, you two boys have meant the world to me. I've tried to do my best to make real men out of you and give you a fighting chance in this world." Sadness covered the father's face now. "I guess it's time for you to find out about life the hard way."

The heartbroken father walked over to his son and gently touched his shoulder.

"Allan, for years I've saved all I could scrape together to make sure that you and Bob would get a college education, but since you're so determined to strike out in life and make your own way, I'm going to give you your share and pray that you will have enough sense to know how to use it."

The young man was elated. He hadn't counted on this bonus in his plans. He was so elated that, as he ran from the room, he didn't hear his father calling after him. It had something to do with always loving him regardless of what happened.

■ ■ ■

Any young man in his right mind wants new wheels. Although it took a chunk out of Allan's stake, he felt it was worth it. The speedy sports car was everything he had ever dreamed of—slick, powerful, and loaded with extras. With a powerhouse like that in his hands and endless miles of roads ahead, how could he miss?

The day Allan left his hometown he felt like he could lick

the world. He stomped the accelerator to the floor, feeling the power, hearing the wind shriek by the window.

"This is the life," he mused to himself. "No more people pushing me around. My life is finally my own."

Allan landed in a large city teeming with people and glittering with possibilities. At first, life there was a lot of fun, but killing time driving around and going to movies soon got old, and Allan started looking around for a little excitement. It wasn't long in coming.

As soon as the word got out that some rich kid was flashing his loot and spending it on anyone that came along, Allan suddenly found himself surrounded by an odd assortment of humanity—all the way from the old man putting the bite on him for a beer to the young kid offering to sell him some grass.

At first Allan was a little frightened by it all, but he soon started to respond. "After all," he said to himself, "I am a man, and I should be free to do what I want. Why not," he bellered, "Why not!"

It was the first time he had gotten drunk, and he felt as though he could lick the world.

■   ■   ■

When Allan finally came to the end of his whirlwind binge, he awoke to find that he was lying on a bare mattress in a filthy one-room shack. The stench of the room pierced his senses. He suddenly realized that his so-called friends were missing, and his money was gone.

The bubble had burst for him. The sports car that he loved had been stolen. Even his shoes were gone. All he had left were foggy memories of days of dissipation.

Allan tried to get a job, but who wants a kid who dropped out of high school? He looked for just any kind of work to stay alive. Hunger was real now, and he could feel the cold.

He finally landed a job cleaning out the slaughter room of a meat factory. It was during one of those moments, as he was mopping up blood and bits of flesh, that he thought of home— of his mom and dad, of his bed with clean sheets, of the laughter of his friends at school.

"Oh, my Lord, I wonder, I wonder if I could go home?"

During the next days the thought came back to him again and again, and it grew stronger:

"Would they let me back? I've wasted everything. I really don't deserve even to be called their son, but maybe, maybe I can go home."

For Allan, the decision to return home was made one night as he lay sick in his shack trembling with cold and burning with fever. Thoughts of home were too much now to turn aside.

"Maybe they still love me enough to take me back. Even if they treated me just as a neighbor's kid, it would be worth it— just to be home."

■ ■ ■

Allan's father was in the driveway of his home working on his car. For days the engine had been giving him trouble, and he figured it had to be in the spark plugs. He glanced up from under the hood for a moment to take a break and noticed at a distance a young man walking toward the house.

He squinted into the bright sun and then turned back to working on his car. Suddenly a piece seemed to fall into place, and he jerked his head up to look again.

"I know that boy," he muttered to himself, "I know him."

Now he noticed the rumpled clothes and disheveled hair, but more than that he felt something—something welling up in him like he'd never felt before. It grew and soared and suddenly burst forth in a shout of exhilaration.

"It's Allan! It's my son—my son!"

The young boy saw his father running toward him. He tried to remember the words that he had rehearsed. He tried to have them ready to pour out the moment his father got to him. Words like: "Pop, I'm sorry. Won't you let me come home?" But before he could get them out, he felt two strong arms around him, and all he could do was weep.

Weep like a man weeps, not a boy. Weep like his father was weeping—with joy.

His father took his face between his rough hands, smearing grease all over his cheeks.

"Son, welcome home." His father choked a little. "Welcome home."

Now a smile broke through the countenance of his father. In that moment Allan came to understand something of the love of his father that had never been real to him before. He came to understand that his father still loved him in spite of it all because he was still his son, flesh of his flesh, bone of his bone.

"Come on in the house, Allan," his father said, tugging at him gently. "Let's get out of those rags and put some solid food in your stomach."

There was joy in Allan's house that night. Even Bob had been called to come home from college and share the moment.

"Allan, a big surprise for you tonight—steaks. I ordered them special, and if you'll go up to your bedroom, you'll find some new clothes that Mom just got back with."

Again his father looked at him intently. "Allan, it's so good to have you back home and with your family. You better hurry up. A lot of your friends are coming over tonight. They have really missed you also."

It was during that party that Bob took his father aside and spoke to him with a mixture of wonder and anger.

"I don't understand, Dad. I'm the one who stayed beside you.

I've used the money you gave me wisely in getting my education—I've helped around the house on the weekends—I've tried not to be a burden to the family by taking a part-time job —and you've never given me a party like this. You've never poured out money on me like you're doing for Allan."

Bob's anger was mounting now. His words exploded.

"My worthless brother turns his back on us, he drops out of school without finishing, he takes off and blows all his money and makes a mess out of his life—and you treat him like a king when he comes crawling back home!"

Bob stood there, every emotion in him charged and on fire. His father came over to him and touched his hand. His voice was strangely mellow.

"Bob, listen to your father, and listen very carefully. I love both of you very deeply—so deeply that sometimes it actually hurts, but Bob, during these past months I knew where you were, and I knew you were man enough to take care of yourself, and I knew you were healthy and fed.

"But your brother I didn't know about. For all I knew he was dead, or hooked on drugs, sick, or lost to us forever . . . . Bob, rejoice with me. Your brother is alive and home, and we must love him back to health. He is alive, Bob! Do you hear me? He's alive, and my whole life is singing and thanking God for that!"

Bob made no reply. The father could only hope that he had come to understand.

"Come on, Son, let's go back in and rejoice that our family is complete again."

Give Up

Luke 18:1–8

It's hard to ignore a nagging woman.

An Honest Appraisal

Luke 18:9–14

Two men came into a church service to worship. One of them, an outstanding deacon, sat on the first pew. The other, a known alcoholic, sat in a far corner in the back.

During the time of meditation the deacon could not help but pray.

"I thank you, God, that I do not have a debauched life like that winebibber that slipped into the service. You know how I attend all the services and tithe my income and serve my community—not like certain people who never give anything. Oh, Lord, it is so good to be so clean and pure inside my soul."

The other man could not do anything but weep and cry out in the agony of his spirit.

"Lord, you know that I can't stand what I am doing to myself and my family. Oh, God, help me! Help me! I need you so badly."

High Cost of Unforgiveness

Matt. 18:21–35

"Okay, I tried it. I really tried it—that turning the other cheek bit; but there's a limit to my patience." Pete was mad.

"How forgiving does a guy have to be? Just give me an outside limit. How about if I forgive a man five times? Even better, make that seven times. Don't you think that would give me the right then to bust him one, or at least quit messing with him?"

That man couldn't help but smile a little at impetuous Peter.

"You won't like what I'm going to say, Pete, but forgiveness isn't something you do a certain number of times. It's a whole attitude towards other people."

An expression of puzzlement flashed across Pete's face. He started to speak but *that man* had anticipated his response.

"Forgive a man seven times, Pete? No, not seven times—but more like seventy times seven, and then some."

Pete was obviously stunned by what appeared to be an unreasonable demand on his tempestuous nature. Again he started to protest, and again *that man* anticipated his frustration.

"Hold on just a moment, Pete. Before you say anything I want to tell you a story . . . .

Some years ago, a certain banker was preparing to retire. Over the space of forty years he had built his small beginnings into a sizable fortune, and now he was ready to wind up a very successful business career.

Because he wanted to leave things in order, he decided that, as a final chore, he would call in all his creditors and see if he couldn't wrap up some outstanding debts and mortgages.

Notices went out, and for weeks the creditors came in to negotiate their loans. The job was almost finished for the retiring banker, but one particular debtor who owed a considerable sum had failed to appear. The banker sent word to him again, and the next morning they met.

"Jim, I don't want to seem unreasonable, but the mortgage on your grocery store has been long overdue. You do realize that we could have closed you out months ago and sold everything in the store to help settle your account?"

"Oh, yes, I know that," the grocer whined, "but you know how tough it's been. That new supermarket that opened a year ago cut the legs out from under a lot of us."

"That's too bad, Jim, but I can't run a bank on charity. I've got to see some cash."

"But you can't expect me to come up with $20,000 out of nowhere," the grocer whined even louder. "I don't have that kind of money."

"I'm really sorry, Jim, but what do you expect me to do?"

"I don't know, but you have carried my business from the very beginning. When you and I started out in this town, you loaned me the money for my shelves and my meat case. I've paid you thousands of dollars in interest alone during these many years." The grocer was pleading now. "Just give me a break, will you?"

The banker stared at him, and suddenly his eyes mellowed, and his voice was filled with something that approached compassion.

"Jim, I know you can't pay it—you'll never be able to pay it; and for that reason I want to do something very special for you."

Jim's head popped up, and his eyes widened.

"All my life, Jim, I've had to be tough to get where I am. I've had to push hard to build this bank; but for once in my life—kinda as a going away present to myself—I'm going to do something unheard of." The banker paused dramatically.

The grocer's curiosity was almost to the breaking point. He slid closer to the edge of his chair.

"Jim, I'm going to wipe your debt off the books. I'm personally going to absorb your mortgage and hand you your grocery store as a gift. Call it what you want, sentimentality or senility, but it's going to be done."

Jim couldn't believe his ears. He sat stunned.

"Do you mean," Jim said with unbelieving wonder, "that you are going to wipe out every cent of my mortgage off the books?"

"That's it, Jim," the banker responded, fully enjoying his moment of magnanimity. "You come by first thing in the morning, and I'll have the mortgage papers and the deed ready to go."

Jim rose slowly and, in a mild stupor, walked out of the banker's office. He just couldn't believe it—every penny he owed wiped off the books.

Climbing into his car, he headed back toward the store. He couldn't wait to share the news with his wife. Over and over he planned how he would surprise her.

As he made a bend in the road his train of thought was interrupted by the sight of an old frame house looming up before him.

"That's Jesse's house," he thought to himself. "I've been meaning to catch up with that old man, and I guess this is as good a time as any."

Jim pulled the car off the road onto a sandy trail leading up to the house. He honked his horn loudly, and a weather-worn old farmer in overalls came out to meet him.

"Jesse, it's time for you to quit avoiding me," the grocer stormed. "Now you and me got a debt to settle."

He climbed out of his car and slammed the door.

"For over four months now you've owed me forty-three dollars on your grocery bill, and all I've been getting are excuses."

"But Mr. Jim," the old man stammered, "you know that I'm good for it. I've never tried to cheat you. Give me a chance. The early crops got killed by the freeze, but in a few months the new crops will be in, and I'll pay you everything I owe."

"A few months!" Jim exploded. "What do you think I run—a charity store? I've got to have some money, and I got to have it now!"

"But, Mr. Jim," the old man protested, "I don't have any. We are down to our last cent."

"We'll see about that," Jim bellered. "Ill get that money if it's the last thing I do."

It was only a few hours later when Jesse was served notice by the sheriff that he was to appear in court to settle his account with the grocer.

The next morning, as Jim walked into the bank, he was feeling like a million dollars. In a few minutes all his troubles would be over. He would walk out of that place the proud owner of a debt-free grocery store.

Jim was escorted directly into the president's office.

"Sit down, Jim," the banker said, motioning him to a big easy chair. He reached into the top drawer of his desk and pulled out some documents.

"Here they are, Jim, signed and witnessed."

The excited grocer bounded up from his chair and made a dash for the desk.

"Wait a minute, Jim," the banker cautioned, "I want to show you something else."

The banker stood to his feet and, taking the papers in his hands, he slowly ripped them into shreds, letting the pieces drift to his carpeted floor.

Jim couldn't believe his eyes. He gave an audible gasp, and his knees weakened. He grabbed for the pieces of paper still floating to the floor.

"What have you done? What have you done?" he groaned, trying to make some sense of the banker's strange action.

The banker stared at him for a long time.

"Why did you do it, Jim?" he finally asked. "What under God's heaven could make you do it?"

"Do what?" Jim whined, "what are you talking about?"

"I'm talking about Jesse!" the banker exploded, slamming the desk with his clenched fist. "Why did you serve papers on Jesse for a piddling forty-three dollars?"

The grocer's eyes were almost glazed now.

"You walked out of this office yesterday afternoon with a $20,000 debt taken off your back and you grabbed an old man around the throat and squeezed him for a few pennies. How could you?"

The banker was getting furious now. His hands trembled as he hit the desk again.

"How could you, Jim? You who had been forgiven of so much, couldn't you forgive another man of so little?"

Jim was trembling now. He started to head for the door.

"Wait a minute. I'm not through with you yet," the banker bellered. "When you get back to your store, you'll find a padlock on the door. I've foreclosed, Jim. With great joy, I've foreclosed, and it's all over. You're wiped out. Now get out and don't ever come this way again looking for help."

Pete looked up at *that man* as he finished. He didn't say anything but just nodded his head in a way that let *that man* know that the message had gotten through.

"Come on, Pete," *that man* said, putting his arm around Pete's shoulder. "Let's go get a cup of coffee."

The Treacherous Tenants

Matt. 21:33-45

There was a building contractor who constructed a worthy apartment house in the middle of a very rough neighborhood.

He left town on a business trip and instructed his business manager to collect the rent in his absence. When he returned, he and his only son had a meeting with the manager and received the disturbing news.

"Boss, I went out there last week," the manager explained, "and tried to collect, but those tenants just laughed in my face and called me everything in the book."

"What did you do?" the boss's son inquired curiously.

"Well, I picked up a few of our men off a construction job and went back in a few days, and, Boss," he said shaking his head, "they were laying for us. I mean they really worked us over. Broke Jake's arm and laid Roy up for a couple of days with some broken ribs."

The contractor was deeply disturbed by this turn of events.

"I didn't fare too well myself," the manager continued reporting. "Took six stitches in my head."

"We've got to stop that nonsense," the contractor stormed. "I guess I'll have to go down and look it over for myself."

At this point the contractor's son who had been listening earnestly interrupted.

"Dad, if you don't mind, I'd like to go for you. I know that section and really care for those people and their problems.

I'd like a little share in helping to work out some kind of solution."

His dad looked at him—again, amazed at his tenderness and concern for others.

"Okay," he finally agreed. "They should respect you—after all you're in the family. Give it a try, but take some men along with you."

"Dad, I'd rather go it alone if you don't mind."

The next day the call came through to the contractor as he was pouring over some blueprints.

"Boss, Boss—your son!" the voice shouted excitedly. "He's been killed! They found his body in an alley near the apartment house early this morning."

The contractor was stunned beyond speaking.

"Boss, Boss," came the concerned voice, "are you all right?"

His voice came back in a whisper.

"I'll get them," he moaned, "so help me—I'll wipe them out if it's the last thing I do; and from this day on those apartments will never house their kind again."

How It Grows

Mark 4:26–29

God's reign among men begins as a gentle whisper of the wind that grows to a gale and, before it culminates, becomes a mighty hurricane.

Rewarding Response

Matt. 13:1–23

"Why should I try anymore?" the young man sighed, "I'm sick of it all—sick of knocking my head against a wall."

This wasn't the first time *that man* had heard the complaint. More and more they were coming to him—discouraged, disappointed, and ready to give up. He always listened with concern and sought to give good advice. The young man continued:

"Do you know what it's like to work for hours preparing a sermon that you feel really will be meaningful to your congregation, only to have them respond with blank stares and superficial nods?"

That man couldn't help smiling to himself. He reflected on his own experiences of preaching to hard heads and glassy eyes.

"Do you know what it does to a fellow to pour out his heart in real concern to someone and get nothing more for his efforts than a bucolic burp?"

That man figured it was time to take away the young man's crying towel and wake him up to a few realities.

"Okay, hold up just a minute," he cut in politely.

The young man stopped short, a little startled by this unexpected interruption of his eloquent complaining.

"What makes you think you deserve people falling all over you in gratitude for your ministry to them?" *that man* challenged.

"Are you serving God because you want to be applauded by men, or because you really love men as God loves them —just as they are with all their faults, failures, and irresponsible actions?"

The young man was not prepared for this peeling of his personality and he winced.

"Sure, you've taken a few beatings—we all have—but you're not responsible for how men respond to your ministry; you're only responsible to be faithful in your ministry."

That man turned to face the young man face on.

"You're a voice for God, offering men life," he pressed emphatically. "You're not his publicity agent, worried about the take at the box office. Once you wake up to that truth, once you see that the ministry is not some glamorous, spotlight performance, then some things can happen."

"What kind of things?" the young man asked hopefully.

"Some exciting, human things," *that man* replied. "I may have sounded hard and unfeeling, but I know how much you want and need acceptance and appreciation—it is only human to want to see some results for all your efforts."

That man walked over to the young man and put his hand on his shoulder.

"Now, even though no man serving God is promised those moments, there are some unexpected joys awaiting a faithful proclaimer of God's love. Let me tell you a story . . . ."

A certain young chemist was moved deeply by the death of a close friend. He couldn't get it out of his mind that his friend's life could have been saved if only the proper equipment had been available—but machines to help failing kidneys were just not sufficiently available, and even those that were in operation were phenomenally expensive and long awaited.

For months the young chemist brooded over this torturing truth until finally, late one evening, he decided it was time to quit tearing his insides out and do something to change the situation.

Utilizing his natural genius, he set out researching the whole field. He interviewed doctors and spent hours with research men, until before long, he started to construct a piece of equipment that he prayed would be portable and economical.

Every spare hour was poured into the project. Finally, after three years, he developed what he considered to be a breakthrough in the field. His excitement could hardly be contained, but he also realized that, before the machine could become operative, it would have to be tested and approved—and that would take money—a lot of money.

At this time the young chemist made a fateful decision —he quit his job and set out full-time to get the backing that he needed.

The young chemist's first appointment was with the president of a large investment company.

"Well, young man," the president began, "I understand that you have a project we might be interested in."

"Yes, Sir," the young chemist responded excitedly. "I'm on the verge of perfecting an important breakthrough in the medical field. It's a small, mechanical machine that will help people with failing kidneys. This little machine will be able to save thousands of lives."

"Is there good money in that kind of thing?" the president pressed. "I mean, can we make a good solid profit?"

"Well," the young chemist replied cautiously, "I'm hoping we can keep the price down so we can make it available to anyone who needs it. That's one of the reasons I'm trying to get it manufactured."

"Yes, but you said it could save lives," the president fired back. "Now tell me, if a man didn't have this gimmick, he'd die—right?"

"Probably, I'm no doctor, but—"

"Well man, we'll have it made," the president interrupted quite excitedly. "A man will do anything to save his life. He'll tap every resource. He'll beg, borrow, or steal. We can name our own price and make a killing."

"I'm sorry," the young chemist replied with irritation, "but you don't get it under those conditions. I'll not bleed any man."

"Okay, sweetheart," the president growled. "If there's not a buck in it for me then I don't want it, so I guess you'd better trot it off to someone else."

"A buck!" the young chemist exploded in anger. "Is that all you can think about? Here I am trying to hand you a gift that will bring life to thousands and you talk about making a buck!"

"Listen, you young pup," the president roared back, leaping to his feet. "Don't try to sell me that 'love for humanity' bit. I don't care about humanity—just me. I didn't get here by loving people. There's only one important thing in life, and that's my life, and neither God nor man is going to tamper with it!"

The young chemist snapped his briefcase shut and strode for the door.

"You may think you're living," he fired back at the president, "but believe me, you're a dead man!"

■ ■ ■

"Oh, me, those precious little children. I can't stand it."
The old woman was actually crying.

The young chemist reflected for a moment on what brought him to this lavish mansion and the near hysterical woman.

His friend had told him, "She's an old kook, but, man, she's loaded. Her old man left her a bundle, and all she does is indulge her emotions in little pet projects. Go give her a try."

"Oh me, oh me," the old woman sobbed again, "We must do something to save those precious lives. Oh, yes, we must get your darling machine to them."

The young chemist was beginning to believe that the old woman really meant it.

"Oh, yes," she continued her heroics, "we must help them. Oh, doctor, we must help them."

"I'm not a doctor," he reminded her.

"Oh, so what?" she replied a little irritated. "You look a lot like one. When I introduce you to my friends, I'll call you 'Doctor.' That will mean so much more to them."

"But I'm not—" the young chemist protested.

"Shush, shush, Doctor," she interrupted. "We must get on with saving the little children."

She waddled over to a large desk, sat down, and pulled out a checkbook.

"Now, Doctor, how much do you need?"

"I'm not sure," the young chemist replied, feeling completely off balance by the woman's action. "I'll need to research the cost figures, manufacturing problems—there's so much."

"Oh, I can't be bothered with all that mishmash. I'll

just give you $10,000 to start with, and, when that runs out, you can come back and get some more."

The young chemist was stunned, really stunned.

"You'll never know how much good your money will do," he said excitedly. "Do you realize how many people in the world will be helped? All kinds of people!"

The old woman scarcely glanced up as she continued writing out the check.

"Doctor, let me make something clear right now." Her tone was strangely serious now. "My money is not to be used to help all people, only certain people."

"What do you mean?" he probed her cautiously.

"I mean, Doctor, that I'm not interested in saving the lives of certain breeds of humanity. My husband couldn't stand them, and I promised him I'd never help them."

"You can't be serious," he replied in stunned fashion. "You don't mean to tell me that you expect me to restrict the use of this machine to only certain kinds of people?"

"That's exactly what I mean," the old woman replied coldly.

"But, I can't—I can't select some to die and some to live! We must offer this life-giving machine to every person."

"Well, Doctor," she replied sternly, "you either do it my way, or you do it without my money."

He stood there for a long moment, staring at her. Then he picked up his hat and sadly headed for the door.

"You're a fool, Doctor," she sputtered sarcastically.

He could hear her ripping the check as he stepped out the door.

■   ■   ■

After three more months of failure it appeared that the young chemist had finally found a backer. He went to meet the committee to get their final recommendation.

"Young man, we really like your project, and we feel that it really has potential."

The young chemist didn't get excited. He had heard that beginning too many times before.

"But, there are some problems."

That was a familiar line to him also.

"We have examined the project from every angle. Now here are some realities you may not know about."

The spokesman went over to a blackboard.

"First, we have got to get the patent secured—that means designing, application fees, research fees, lawyers. Right off the bat we're going to have some tough sledding."

The young chemist's first impulse was to leap to his feet and yell out that the end result was worth all the effort, but he restrained himself.

"And then, if we can get the patent," the spokesman continued, "we will have to get it approved for medical purposes. And after the prototype is approved there's manufacturing and distribution . . . ."

The young chemist couldn't take it any longer.

"Will you just come out and tell me what you're driving at? I don't need an easy letdown."

"Okay, the plain fact is we don't want to mess with it. There are just too many complications and problems that have to be worked out before we can bring it off."

"You mean to tell me," the young chemist questioned, "that the potential of this machine isn't great enough in

your opinion to be worth fighting through all the head-
aches?"

"That just about sums it up," the spokesman replied,
"I'm sorry, but we're just not prepared for that uphill
climb, no matter what lies at the end. That's it—clear and
simple."

■   ■   ■

If it hadn't been for that phone call, the young chemist
would have given it up. He had become discouraged and
disillusioned. It seemed hopeless to continue.

"Jim, I think I've got something for you."

He recognized the voice of one of the men he used to
work with some years ago.

"For the past few months I've been talking to an engi-
neering firm here in the city about the possibility of backing your project and, Jim, they are really interested. I've
set up an appointment for you for Friday night."

Needless to say, Jim was there, but this time he sensed
that things were going to be different.

"You see, Jim, we figure that, if the idea is feasible,
we can absorb a lot of the cost and overhead by utilizing
the facilities of our own company. We even have a manufacturing division that can mass produce the machine."

For the first time in over a year the young chemist was
beginning to believe that it would really happen.

"We're really excited about the possibility. We are all
in agreement that we could make a fair profit on the project, but most of all we'd be doing something in a tangible
way to save human lives."

The young chemist tried to speak, but the moment was
too much for him.

"Now, let's get down to the details. I need to know every facet of your work."

The day the contracts were signed was exciting indeed, as was the day the patent was granted and the machine approved for medical purposes, but the final reward was yet to come.

It happened late one evening. The phone's ring shook the young chemist out of bed.

"Jim, it's working! Thank God it's working! I'm down here at City General Hospital. They hooked us up with a child in critical condition, and Jim, it's working!"

All the young chemist could do was sob like a little child.

"Get down here quick, Jim, I want you to be a part of this. I want you to see the joy on the parents' faces and the smile on that child's. Jim, do you realize that this is just the beginning—do you realize how many thousands of lives will be saved and how many times you're going to thank God that you stuck with it?"

He hung up the phone, threw his body across the bed, and sighed deeply.

"Lord, it's been worth every ache, every doubt, and every disappointment."

That man looked into the eyes of the young minister.

"Son, you might as well know the truth. As long as you serve God, you'll meet those who will reject your offer of God's love completely. You'll encounter those who will get emotionally charged up for a while and then drift off. You'll tangle with

those who want no responsibility and will reject all commit-
ment to service. But, listen, and listen carefully—every once in
a while, through it all, you will see a glimmering. You will see
a hand reach out in need, and you will touch it with the message of God's love, and in that moment, when you realize that
God has used you as an instrument of his love and healing
power, you will say with joy:

" 'Lord, it has been worth it all. I have my reward.' "

Revealing Test

". . . but, how is it possible to tell those who belong to God from those who are only pretending?"

■ ■ ■

The distinguished dealer in fine arts and antiques was furious.

"Never, in my thirty years of business," he steamed, "have I ever been the target for such a fraudulent practice!"

He had just been informed that some of the marble sculptures he was importing from Europe were defective.

The discovery came quite accidentally. During the unpacking of the crates, one of the assistants noticed a pitted area on a bust that was a sure sign of poor craftsmanship. The sculptor had tried to cover up his slipshod work by filling the gap with clear wax. When it was hardened and polished over, it became almost impossible to detect the flaw in the sculpture.

"Wait until I get up with the firm that planted those pieces in my collection," he continued, stewing. "Such an old stunt, too. Any sculptor worth his salt wouldn't go near that gimmick."

The owner made a move for his telephone.

"Trying to sell me haphazard work like that as top-quality pieces—wait till I get my lawyer on their backs."

His assistant interrupted him at this point.

"Wait a minute, Sir. Think with me," he started quietly. "What are we going to prove? We've got literally thousands of pieces of sculpture. We can't possibly go over each one of them inch by inch to test for flaws."

The owner started to calm down as the assistant continued.

"If we make a big issue over this one piece of defective work, they can claim it was just an oversight in the shipping department."

The simple truth of the situation started to dawn on the dealer. He realized how very difficult, indeed, it would be to examine every piece by hand.

"What do you suggest that we do, Hiram?" he asked in a quandary. "How am I going to sell any of it?"

"I don't know, Sir, I really don't know." He finally came out with what they both had been thinking: "I guess it will mean a pretty big loss for you no matter what happens."

It was late that night, after hours of turning in his sleep, that the solution came to the dealer.

"So simple—so very simple," he muttered. "But it will work. I know it will."

He was so elated with his plan that he awoke his assistant from his sleep to set the arrangements in motion.

"Hiram, I want you to put that creative mind of yours to work and come up with the most extravagant promotion we've ever had for a sculpture exhibition and sale."

Hiram was still trying to shake the cobwebs out of his mind and figure out what his boss was talking about.

"Sir, pardon me if I sound a little thick," he said, "but you're not talking about a promotion for that collection with the defective pieces?"

"Yes, I am, Hiram," he fired back excitedly. "We're going to give all those works top billing and put them on the market for top prices."

"But, Sir," Hiram replied with growing concern, "you know

that we will be selling some defective pieces as quality sculpture, and—"

"Don't argue with me, Hiram," the dealer exploded. "Just get to work on the exhibition."

"But, Sir," he cautioned again, "how can you sell that collection and still maintain your integrity as a dealer?"

"Hiram, I'm not going to spend the rest of the night arguing with you," the dealer fumed with exasperation. "Just do as I say."

"All right, Sir," he replied in subdued tones. "But I'm not so certain that this won't be my last responsibility with you and the firm."

"We'll talk about that later, Hiram," the dealer responded.

"Yes, Sir," he replied sadly. "Now if you'll excuse me, I need to get a little rest."

"Sure thing, Hiram," the dealer chuckled, "Oh, by the way, when you lay out your plans, there's just one thing special I'd like you to include for my sake."

"What is it, Sir?" he asked.

"I want you to make arrangements to fly in all the sculptors that have had anything to do with the collection . . . and I also want you to make sure that every piece of sculpture is labeled with the name of the man who created it."

Hiram was really dazed now. Not only was the dealer going to pawn off defective pieces of sculpture, but it appeared as though he was going to honor the dishonest sculptors at the same time.

The dealer's voice cut into his stunned silence. "One last thing, Hiram. I want this exhibition to take place outdoors in a garden setting."

"In a what!" Hiram gasped.

"You heard me . . . in a garden!" the dealer roared back.

"Plan the exhibition to open about noon, but don't terminate any sales until about four in the afternoon. Do you understand?"

"Yes, Sir. Even though I don't understand—I understand."

"Okay, Hiram, now you can go back to sleep."

The day of the exhibition dawned with expectancy. Never had the art world buzzed with such excitement. Famous sculptors, millions of dollars in marble, dignitaries,—all the elements needed to make this the social highlight of the year.

To top it all off, it turned out to be a beautiful summer day. Not a cloud in the sky. The sun glowed in all its glory as it streamed warmth to every section of that garden.

The dealer stood beside his assistant.

"Hiram, you have done a magnificent job in preparing this exhibition. I do thank you very much."

"Sir, if you'll pardon my saying it," he said sadly, "I still cannot justify what you are doing. It's simply not like you at all."

"Hiram, I really appreciate your concern," the dealer said in sympathetic tones. "I haven't forgotten that fraudulent pieces are scattered throughout that collection, but, Hiram, you can put your mind at ease—I've taken care of that problem."

Hiram was really confused now and couldn't help but blurt out: "What do you mean?"

"You'll see, Hiram," the dealer said smiling. "Very shortly now it will all become clear to you."

The answer started to dawn on Hiram about three oclock that afternoon. He first noticed it on a bust of Homer. At first it looked like a tear on the bust, or possibly a drop of rain— but when he touched it, it was soft and hot.

"Wax!" he thought excitedly to himself. "That's wax!"

He glanced quickly into the sky and for the first time became aware of how intensely the sun was blazing down on the marble pieces. Blazing so hot that the wax hidden in flawed places started to melt under its incessant heat, revealing and exposing all the pits and chips and defective cuts.

It suddenly hit him like a thunderbolt.

"All the pieces are being exposed to the heat of the sun, and every defective piece will be revealed!"

At that moment he heard the dealer's voice ringing out over the loudspeaker system.

"May I have your attention, please." His voice sounded forth gravely. "We have made a startling discovery that comes as a shock to us all."

The people started to gather in close to the podium.

"I have been informed that many of the statuary that are on exhibition here have been waxed over to cover up poor workmanship."

A murmur went through the knowledgeable crowd.

"But, the long exposure of these pieces to the sun has made the defective pieces easily identifiable."

So true. The wax was now flowing freely from all the defective works.

"I know that none of us that love the arts can bear to put up with dishonesty in our ranks," the dealer continued somberly. "Therefore, I am ordering that all these defective pieces be destroyed and that all the sculptors whose names appear on them be put under arrest, along with those firms responsible for this fraud."

A Big Conclusion

Matt. 13:31–32

God's reign among men begins like an insignificant acorn that is tossed about by squirrels and the elements, but grows to a mighty oak that provides shelter for many.

How It Flavors

Matt. 13:33–35

God's reign among men permeates like a clove of garlic in a fine spaghetti sauce.

At All Cost

Matt. 13:44

The reign of God in a man's life is to be desired like a man who gets an inside tip on the stock market and invests every cent he can get his hands on.

A Priceless Possession

Matt. 13:45–46

The reign of God in a man's life is to be sought with the fervor of a man who discovers a priceless antique in a junk shop and sells all he has in order to purchase it.

Picking Time

Matt. 13:47–50

God's reign among men is like a conveyor belt carrying freshly picked peaches. The packers pluck from the conveyor all the rotting fruit and send it to the pigpens, but the good fruit they pack for shipment.

A New Joy

Matt. 13:51–53

A man who opens his life to God's reign is like a child discovering life and all its adventure for the first time.

The Generous Farmer

Matt. 20:1–16

God's reign among men is measured by God's standards.

■ ■ ■

A farmer went out early in the morning, before daybreak, to the village square to hire some men to work his tomato fields.

"What kind of wages are you paying?" he was asked.

"Don't worry about that," he replied with a wave of his hand. "I'm as fair a man as you'll find in this county."

"That's not good enough for me," one of the laborers fired back. "I got to know right now what I'll be making, or you can count me out. There are other farms that need help around here you know."

"Okay, since you insist on a guarantee," the farmer sighed, "I'll pay you seventeen dollars for the day and provide all your meals. That's as good a wage as you'll make anywhere in this county."

He found four men who would agree to work the fields on that basis and drove them to the work site. They arrived just as the sun was breaking over the rows of tomatoes. It would be scorching hot before the sun went down again.

Later that morning the farmer drove back around the village square on the way to pick up a load of fertilizer and noticed some other men sitting on the benches. He stopped the truck.

"Hey, fellows," he called from the truck, "why are you sitting around?"

"Don't seem to be much work today," one replied dejectedly. ". . . And I sure could use the money."

"Well, I could use some more help in my tomato fields," the farmer stated calmly. "How about working for me the rest of the day?"

The men dashed off the benches and scrambled into the back of the pickup truck.

As the truck sped off toward the farm, one of the laborers yelled out to the farmer:

"What kind of wages are we going to be making?"

"Don't worry about that," the farmer yelled back into the wind whirling by his window. "Whatever is fair you'll get."

"That's okay by us," another yelled back, "just so we get some work."

It was early afternoon when the farmer received word that a hail storm might brew up later that day; and that could only mean severe damage to his tomato crops.

He decided to get as much of his fields picked as possible. Driving back to the village he felt fortunate to find more laborers waiting in the square.

"Hey, fellows," the farmer called out. "How about an afternoon of work?"

They scrambled on board, thankful for the good fortune that came their way.

"Say, you fellows haven't asked me how much I'll pay," the farmer called to them as they settled down in the back of the truck.

"We're not worried about that," one of them replied happily. "Any work is better than no work, and anything we make is more than we had sitting around killing time."

The farmer couldn't help but smile to himself.

The afternoon went by hurriedly. The tomato crop was being rushed to a safe spot, and it appeared as though the storm might hold off altogether.

The farmer was in the fields supervising the work when he noticed a young man coming through the crops toward him. He walked over to meet him.

"Are you the owner of the farm?" the boy inquired cautiously.

"Yes, I am. What can I help you with?"

"Well, Sir, I'd like some work," he requested quietly. "I had been looking all day without much luck, and then I heard that you were hiring extra hands."

"It's almost evening," the farmer reminded him. "We'll be through in another hour. You won't get much time in."

"I really don't care, Sir. I've come this far, and I figure that an hour's work is better than none. I'd been here sooner, but I had to walk it, and it's quite a way out here."

"Okay, get out there," the farmer instructed. "Ask the man in the straw hat what you should be doing."

■   ■   ■

At the end of the long day the laborers gathered to collect their wages. They were amazed to discover that the farmer was paying all those who came late to work a full day's wage, seventeen dollars.

The young man who worked for only an hour was especially taken off balance by this strange act.

"But, I don't deserve a full day's pay," he stuttered. "I've only been out there for—"

"Now don't argue with me," the farmer interrupted him gently. "I set the wages around here, not you."

When those who had been hired first early in the morning came to receive their wages, they were elated.

"How about that," one whispered to the others. "If he's paying them seventeen dollars for part-time work, we're going to make a killing since we were out there all day."

They were astonished, though, to find out that, when they reached the farmer, he handed them seventeen dollars each.

"Wait a minute!" exploded one of them. "You've given me only seventeen dollars!"

"Yeah, what kind of robbery is this?" another bellered. "We work hard all day, and you pay us the same that you paid that kid who worked only a measly hour!"

The farmer sat there quietly, listening to the violent outbursts with a peaceful countenance.

"Listen, we won't be taken like this!" another thundered. "We've sweated through the heat of that scorching sun. We did most of the dirty work. We expect our dues!"

The farmer had just about enough. He slammed his fist down on the crate serving as his desk.

"Stop your whining," he cut in matter-of-factly. "When I hired you to work, you were the ones who insisted on a contract before you'd come. I told you then that I was a fair man—and fair I am. I'll not cheat you. Seventeen dollars a day is what you bargained for and agreed to, and seventeen dollars is what you're going to get. Never let it be said that I ever welshed on a contract with any of my laborers."

The men stood there, stunned by the farmer's remarks.

"Now pick up the things that belong to you, and I'll give you all a ride back to the square."

As he dropped them off he gave them a few closing words.

"Just remember that your wages were fair. If I want to be generous beyond that point, that's my business. If I want to give to the last like I gave to the first, that's my concern—but remember, every one of you, that regardless of whether you were first or last, you all got the best wages available in this county."

Always Be Ready

Matt. 24:43–45

No man knows which year his income tax return will be checked, so he should always be prepared to give an account of his actions.

The Deadly Mistake

Matt. 25:1–13

God's reign among men culminates in a most unexpected
way . . .

■ ■ ■

"But I tell you they are coming for us! Any day now they will
be showing up!"

He shouted in order to be heard over the sound of the heavy
artillery.

"Yeah, yeah, I've been hearing that for weeks now," the second soldier spat back, ". . . and still no action."

The two men had been pinned down with their company for
several days now. Fortunately they had a strong position and so
held off the enemy.

They had been promised that they would be airlifted out as
soon as possible, but the days had dragged on, and the fighting
was getting heavier.

"Look," the first soldier argued, "the rescue will come, and
we've got to be ready to make a dash for it when it happens.
There will be no time to lose."

"Quit your moaning," the second soldier mocked. "There's
no rescue coming, and I'm not going to waste my time getting
ready for some kind of wild dash through enemy fire across an
open field for a rescue that will never come off."

"Well, you should," the first soldier gibed. "You just don't
seem to care. For instance, where's your helmet? I haven't seen

it on you for days. You know that one bullet could finish you off."

"If you must know," came the sarcastic answer, "I planted petunias in it. I'll never need it in this hole anyway."

"And your equipment—what about it? I haven't seen you clean your gun in days. If it should jam up on you in the middle of close fire, you're a dead man."

"Big deal—you really scare me," the soldier continued mockingly. "Why don't you just relax and admit that we're stuck here for a long time? Nobody is going anywhere. We're not going to see any big action."

The next few days dragged on with spasmodic fire. The first soldier was beginning to believe that his cynical friend might be right. No action and no rescue in sight.

It was during the early hour of the morning when it happened. A loud explosion broke the early morning silence, and flares lit the sky.

"Enemy attack!" the word swept through the camp like wildfire. "They're trying a sneak attack! All out! All out! We're going to have to fight for our lives!"

By the time the troops were armed and assembled, the enemy was sweeping down on them in overwhelming waves. The soldiers could only anticipate their being overridden and annihilated. It was at that moment that the sound of a thousand whirling birds could be heard.

"Look! To the east! In the sky!" an excited yell rang out. "It's our choppers. They've come to pull us out."

A cheer went through the company as they started to scramble for the helicopters that were landing in an open clearing about a hundred yards away.

The two soldiers who had been arguing bout the rescue several days before suddenly found themselves apparently cut off from rescue by a group of enemy soldiers who approached close to them.

"Come on," the first soldier yelled to the other. "We'll have to go through them before it's too late."

"What do you mean?" the soldier said, trembling. "How are we going to get through those guys?"

"Fight through them, stupid," he yelled again. "Now fix your bayonet, get your helmet on, and make sure that gun is loaded to maximum—and let's get out of this hole!"

"But, I can't . . ." the soldier said.

"Can't!" the voice roared at him. "Man, we've got to get out of here—and now!"

"But you know I don't have my helmet," he whined. "I can't go into that gunfire without some protection—"

"You better go just like you are—or it's curtains," he roared at the frightened man again. "I'm not kidding you—playtime is over!"

"But I've lost my bayonet."

"That's tough," he fired back, "but I'm not waiting around. You better grab your gun and take your chances."

The frightened soldier cried out again: "I don't have any ammunition. I didn't bother to replenish after that skirmish yesterday that cleaned me out."

"You mean you've got an empty gun?" the soldier asked.

"No ammunition . . ." he muttered, as though in a trance. "Please help me—give me some of yours."

"Listen, you can whine all you want, but I've got one clip in this gun and that's going to carry me through to that chopper."

"Help me," the soldier pleaded.

"I'm sorry, but I warned you days ago to be ready."

"But I didn't believe it," he whined again. "I thought it was just a game. Please help me."

"I'm sorry. There's nothing I can do. You can follow me out if you want and try to stay behind me, but I can't wait any longer. Those guys are almost on top of us."

The soldier jumped out of the hole onto the open field, his gun spitting lead as he dashed for safety and the chopper.

The other soldier slumped to the bottom of the foxhole clutching his empty gun to his livid face.

The sound of the approaching soldiers was clear now.

"I didn't believe it would happen," he whimpered. "I didn't believe it . . ."

The Landowner's Challenge

Matt. 25:14–30

A large landowner was going overseas for a year to supervise the development of some farmland for the government.

Before leaving he called his top hands in for a conference.

"You men have been with me for a long time, but always in the capacity of taking orders. Now I want to give you a real chance to prove the kind of stuff that you are made of."

The men were immediately aroused by the words of their boss, but they had learned to respect his business mind and unusual approach to problems.

"I'm leaving all of you with some land I want you to develop," he continued. "I don't care what you do with it, but, when I come back, I expect to see that you have turned it into a good profit for the ranch."

"That's great, Boss," one of the men cut loose. "Sounds like a real challenge."

"We'll see," he said with a smile. "I'll certainly get a real understanding into the kind of men you are."

"What kind of help do we get, Boss?" another inquired.

"All you need will be at your disposal. My equipment, the stock, the whole works. Just keep a close record of your expenditures so I can get an accurate reading on how well you all did."

"When do we get started?" one of them asked excitedly.

"Immediately," he fired back. "I leave in the morning, and you're on your own for the next twelve months."

The landowner walked over to a large wall map of the ranch lands.

"Now for your assignments."

The men crowded close to him in order to get a good look at the property they would be tending.

"Ben, I'm going to assign you this 500 acres on the south end," he said, sweeping his hand across the map. "I know some of it is mountain, but there should be plenty for you to use your ingenuity on."

"Thanks, Boss," he replied with enthusiasm. "You can count on me."

"Now, Hank, I'm assigning you this 200 acres on the west side of the ranch. It's near the river, so it should be looked on as a prize catch. Give it your best effort."

"No sweat, Boss," he replied smiling. "You've got no worries. I'll make that property really pay off before the year is over."

"That leaves you, Wilt," the landowner continued. "Come closer to the map."

The employee moved in close to his boss.

"Wilt, I want you to take this ten acres located right here around the springs. I know it doesn't sound like much, but that's great land and will really pay off if you put your mind to it."

He took a long look at Wilt. "Think you can handle it?"

"Sure, I guess so," he replied cautiously. "Shouldn't be too much trouble."

"Okay, fellows, you've got your assignments," he said with a satisfied sigh. "I wish you all the very best luck. See you in about twelve months."

■　■　■

The year passed swiftly, and it seemed no time at all before the landowner was back stateside. After getting settled, he called his top hands in for supper and a report.

"I can't tell you how much I missed my spread," he sighed after supper, settling back into his favorite chair.

"Boss, it's great to have you back," one of the men said enthusiastically, "we've really missed you around here."

After filling in the landowner on the ranch in general, the conversation finally came around to their assignments and how they came out.

"Okay, Ben, you had the biggest assignment" he said, waving a hand indicating him to sit down. "Let's hear how you did."

"Well, Boss, you were right about that 500 acres being mountainous. More than I realized. I thought about putting out crops at first, but I had to scratch that—too many boulders and trees to clear out to make it a profitable adventure within a year's time."

The landowner was caught up in Ben's analysis. He had figured crops wouldn't make it also, so he was especially curious to find out what other route Ben had taken.

"So, Boss, after several other alternatives didn't work out, I finally hit on a solution."

"What did you come up with, Ben?" he couldn't help but ask out loud.

"Goats!" he said with a smile.

"Goats!" the landowner exclaimed, "Come on, Ben, don't pull my leg."

"Right, Boss, goats!" he continued, his smile growing. "But a very special breed I imported from Europe. Their skins bring a fantastic return in the interior decorating market."

"Can you imagine that," the landowner said. "Goats, of all things!"

"Right, and the land is perfect for their grazing habits. I've already paid for them out of the first six months' profits, and we will double our original investment before the year is out."

The landowner slapped his knee. "I'd have never believed it —goats! That's great, Ben, absolutely great. I couldn't be more pleased. Okay, Hank. Let's see if you can top that."

"Well, Boss, I don't know if I can top it, but I think you'll be pleased."

"Okay, try me," the landowner said teasingly.

"You were right about that 200 acres being good land. I figured I could irrigate it from the river and raise some really good crops."

"Well, did you?"

"Yes, in a sense, Boss," he replied cautiously, "but in another sense I didn't."

"Wait a minute, Hank. You're getting me confused."

"Well you see, Boss, I didn't figure just raising crops would be a very exciting challenge, and I also wasn't sure I could really make the profit I wanted with the run-of-the-mill stuff we grow around here."

"Okay, Hank, I give up," the landowner said with good humor, "what did you do?"

"Don't laugh, Boss."

"I won't laugh, Hank," he replied, his curiosity really peaked to the breaking point now.

"Well, I raised—popcorn!"

"You what?" the landowner exploded in laughter.

"You promised you wouldn't laugh."

"Well, Hank, I'm sorry, but you caught me a little off balance. Now go over that again."

"Popcorn, Boss. I'm raising popcorn."

"I know, but what good is it? Did you find some company that will take it off your hands?"

"Sure did, Boss," he replied with a smug smile, "sure did."

"Well, don't keep me waiting," he pursued. "Is it one here in the state?"

"Well, yes, Sir. It is now. In fact, it's a new company."

"A new one?" the landowner echoed cautiously. "Whose?"

"Yours, Boss."

"Mine?" he sputtered, completely off balance now.

"Yes, Sir—yours," he replied with satisfaction. "You see, Boss, I figured it would make us a good investment. We grow and package our own, and, Boss, we've already swept across the state and going great guns. In fact, it's named after your ranch."

"Well, I'll be," he exclaimed, completely overwhelmed by this way-out investment.

"We're making a killing, Boss. More than doubled our investment already."

The landowner couldn't get over it. He sat there for a few moments reflecting on the shrewd business move. Finally, he turned to Wilt.

"Okay, Wilt, the other reports are in. Let's hear how you made out."

A strange quiet had fallen over the other men. The landowner sensed it immediately.

"Well, Boss," Wilt started quietly, "I don't have much to report."

"What do you mean, Wilt," he questioned. "I left you with ten of the best acres I've got on this ranch. What did you do with them?"

"To be honest, boss," he stuttered, "I didn't do anything."

"Come on, Wilt," he said with unbelief. "Quit kidding me. What did you do with the land?"

"Boss, don't get mad at me," he pleaded, "I know how tough you are about business deals, and I was afraid to take a chance with your investment. I mean, look at it from my angle—suppose I put stock on the land, and they got killed, or I put out crops and they got wiped out, then what would you have done to me? I'd be in a sorry mess trying to make up all that loss, so I just sat on the land."

He noticed the anger welling up in the landowner.

"It's all right though, Boss. The land is in good shape. I've kept it mowed and—"

"You mean to tell me," the landowner interrupted with a vengeance, "that during this past year you haven't even tried to turn a profit on that land?"

"Well, Boss, it's not that big a deal—just a little land. You gave Ben 500 acres and Hank 200. What's a lousy ten acres? If I'd had what they had, maybe I could have done some pretty big things, too."

"Listen, Wilt, they got those acres because they were men enough to handle them, but you got ten acres because that's all you are capable of handling—and you couldn't even come up to that small challenge."

The employee was beginning to feel the pressure now. He started to tremble ever so slightly.

"Don't gripe about their acres," the landowner continued, pouring it on. "The more a man has, the more courage, guts, and sense of responsibility it takes to handle it. I'm not angry with you because you tried and failed—I'm angry because you you didn't have guts enough to use what was given to you—you did nothing, Wilt. Do you hear me—nothing!"

Wilt was shaking fully now. He hadn't expected this kind of response from his employer.

The landowner turned to the other men at this point.

"When I left, I set a test before you men. Ben, you and Hank have been faithful over your assignment—now I'm going to make you owners of much. The land you managed is now yours to keep."

The men stood there in stunned silence.

"But, Wilt, your land is taken away from you and split between the other two. You can pack up and pull out as fast as you can. I have no room for a man who lets my gift to him lie fallow and unproductive."

Substitute Guests

Luke 14:16–24

A certain man made plans to celebrate his fiftieth wedding anniversary with a luxurious banquet at the Conrad Hilton. The invitation list was made out carefully so as to include all those who had been closest to the couple through the past years. No one was forgotten—the minister who had married them, the doctor who delivered their children, their first neighbors, his business partners and associates, and even the grocer who had given them credit during those early difficult days.

How excited the couple were as the night of the banquet came upon them! For days they had been preparing for this once-in-a-lifetime event. She dressed out in a beautiful gown especially prepared for the occasion. Her silvery hair sparkled, reflecting the hours she had spent at the beauty parlor; and the old gentleman—well, he was simply elegant in his black tuxedo and top hat.

They arrived at the Conrad Hilton early in order to make sure that everything was in readiness. The ballroom shimmered in preparation. The chef was anxiously preparing to broil hundreds of prime steaks to perfection. The waiters were instructed and keenly aware of all the details to make the meal an unforgettable event.

The old gentleman sighed with satisfaction and settled back to wait for the first guests to arrive.

Within a few moments one of the waiters came up to him.

"You just had a phone call, Sir. Mr. Harbing called to say that he will be unable to attend."

"Oh, sorry to hear that." The old gentleman meditated a moment. "You know he was the one that introduced me to my wife. I sure hope he's not sick."

"Nothing like that, Sir," the waiter replied. "He said that he had just bought a new outboard motorboat and was going to run down to the coast tonight so he could try it out in the morning."

The hurt that flashed across the old gentleman's face was obvious to those around. Before he could say anything else, a bellhop appeared.

"This message was left for you at the desk."

He tipped the bellhop and opened the letter.

"Sam, we sure are sorry we can't be with you tonight. Alice and I have a couple of tickets to see *Man from La Mancha,* and we just couldn't afford to miss it. You know how tough it has been to get in. You and Betty have a good time. We sure do remember how we struggled together during those early days when business was so tough."

Before the shock could wear off the old gentleman, his wife came running up to him, obviously upset.

"Sam, I just got a call from Janet. You know how close we have been for these past years, and how much I wanted her to share this evening with me.

"Sam, she's not coming. This is her bridge night, and she's not coming!" She was close to tears now.

"Sam, none of our friends are coming."

The old gentleman was mad now—fighting mad. He hugged his wife close to him.

"Honey, don't you worry. We're going to have the biggest and most memorable evening this city has ever seen."

He called over the waiters, reached into his pocket, and pulled out a roll of bills.

"Listen fellows, I want you to hustle inside and outside this hotel. I want you to hit the streets and alleys. I want you to corner people and get them here. I don't care if they are rich or poor, lame or blind, stinking or deodorized—but I want this banquet hall packed to celebrate our anniversary."

The old man took a deep breath and walked back to his wife. He was hurt and disappointed that those closest to him would not be sharing this celebration with him.

He looked to the main entrance and saw the first of many new guests arriving.

"Come on, Honey, let's greet our new friends. Even though we don't know them now, in a moment we will know them, for they have accepted our invitation to join our celebration."

A Look At the Goats

Matt. 25:41–46

The visitation chairman of a very prominent church was deeply concerned that his people were not seeing more results for their efforts. He called a meeting of all his staff and helpers to examine the situation.

"We are not getting the additions to our membership we ought to be seeing," he stated in somber tones. "I aim to find out why before this meeting is over."

He walked over to the blackboard and started dashing off a series of dates and figures.

"If you'll notice, we are running 21% behind the number of new members we experienced by this time last year; and we are 32% behind our projected overall goal for this year."

He paused for a moment, tapping the board with the piece of chalk.

"Now, I have analyzed this situation carefully, and I have discovered that the problem is not that we aren't making enough visits. In fact we are ahead of last year's record in this department."

Again he paused, relishing that little bit of good information that he had in his files.

"The problem is," he continued, "that we are not getting a high enough percentage of additions from these visits."

He paused to stare at a light fixture.

"Now either you're not doing a good job selling the church,

or else you're wasting a lot of time with some poor possibilities for church membership—now which is it?"

There was a long silence. An uneasy air settled over the group. Finally, one little lady spoke up.

"Well," she piped, "I had a terrible experience this month."

"Well, now we're going to get down to it," the chairman thought happily.

"You know that Norman family we were all so interested in getting? Well, I must have made six visits. Called them almost every day on the telephone and even sent them cards through the mail; and last week they had the audacity—after all I had done—to join another Baptist church."

The little woman was obviously disturbed by this breach of etiquette.

"And I even warned them about that church. I told them what a liberal that pastor was and how that church wasn't big enough to afford air-conditioned facilities like ours; but they joined anyway."

She paused for a moment, relishing her dramatic moment.

"I've never been so hurt. That was five additions—two adults and three children—that slipped right through my fingers."

The visitation chairman interrupted her at this point.

"I know that was a tough one to lose," he sighed. "What a waste of time!"

He was contemplating the bitter experience when another voice cut into his meditation.

"You think that's bad. Let me tell you something I still haven't gotten over."

The man speaking was one of the chairman's very best visitors so everyone was riveted to his every word.

"You remember that about a month ago we showed that Billy Graham film for the teen-agers?"

Everyone nodded his head knowingly.

"Well, that night there were a couple of kids from a Johnson family who came with some of our members."

He stopped to make sure all were giving him their full attention.

"That night at the invitation those two came up and took Jesus as their Savior."

Again the nodding indicated that they all remembered the occasion.

"Well, the very next day I got those cards they filled out when they came forward. I headed for their house that night to see about getting them baptized into the membership; and that's when it happened."

"What happened?" one little lady gasped out without realizing what she was doing.

"Well," he continued, building up the drama, "the parents of those children fought me every step of the way."

The old man was beginning to warm up now.

"You know how it is when there are parents who are not interested in the welfare of their children. I begged with them, pleaded. I did everything I knew to do, but nothing availed."

The visitation chairman cut in excitedly.

"But if they still haven't been baptized maybe we could send out a new team and wear those parents down. Maybe we haven't lost them yet for our membership. A couple of additions by baptism would certainly help things look up a little around here."

"No! No! That's what I'm trying to tell you!" the old man stormed back impatiently. "In spite of everything I did, in spite of all my preaching and pleading, those parents had so warped the minds of those children that the kids wanted to be baptized into the Methodist church where the parents attend."

A deep sigh shuddered through the man's slight frame.

"It was one of the bitterest moments of my life."

A new voice was heard from the group at this point.

"Since we are all sharing our disappointments, I guess I'll have to add mine."

She was new at this visitation work but showed great promise. She had already received a reputation for being tenacious. Once she was on the trail of a prospect, something had to happen. She just didn't give up.

"All of you," she continued, "have been in the work a lot longer than I have, and you have learned to take disappointments, but this experience really hurt me deeply."

They all leaned toward her sympathetically.

"About two months ago I was assigned the Hawkins family. I think you all remember them. The husband was with an insurance firm. Wife bleached her hair. They had four children —two already baptized and two kind of young, but we probably could have worked them in for baptism, although I'm not sure about the five-year-old. He was a little—"

"Go on with the story," the visitation chairman broke in irritably.

"Well, one of the older children was confined to a wheelchair. Some disease she had since childhood."

"Tch, tch," a sympathetic voice was heard.

"So I figured that she would be the key to reach the family. If I could center my attention on that crippled child, then the family would be obligated to join."

"Good thinking!" an anonymous voice rang out.

"That's the way I started," she continued. "I brought the girl little gifts and candy. I even baby-sat with her while her mother went off to do the grocery shopping. You have no idea how much effort and time I put into that particular situation."

"What happened?" the lady sitting beside her blurted out.

"Well, I figured that I had just about wrapped them up. They were showing up every Sunday just as regular as clockwork. In fact, the mother had told me that they had decided to join, and I was betting that this Sunday would do it."

"What happened? What happened?" the little lady popped up again, getting more exasperated.

"The bottom fell out, that's what happened," she burst forth excitedly. "It's all over."

The room fell deadly silent for a moment, and then that incessant voice!

"But what happened?"

The young thing figured the moment had come to let them all share her grief.

"Last night the husband came home and gave them the news," she moaned. "He's been transferred. They're moving out of the city within two weeks."

"Oh, no!" the little old lady exclaimed.

"Oh, yes," the young thing sighed. "And just imagine all the time I wasted with that crippled child."

"That is too bad," the visitation chairman comforted. "We all know how you feel, but that's part of being a servant for Jesus. Now, if I could interrupt these heartbreaking testimonies for a moment, I want to ask a few questions about some of these reports on my desk."

The visitation chairman took out a pair of glasses and adjusted them on his nose.

"Miss Lightfoot, I notice a family on your visitation report that I'm not familiar with—a Stinson family."

"Oh, yes," the young thing replied excitedly. "I've been visiting them for about three months."

"Three months!" the visitation chairman responded with

surprise. "Why haven't we seen some results by this time. Are they giving you a lot of trouble?"

"Oh, no, Sir, not at all; but you see they live on the east side of town—"

"East side!" he interrupted vigorously, "Isn't that a kind of poverty area?"

"Well, not exactly," she replied slowly. "They are mostly lower income families, but they work hard at making a living and keeping their heads above water."

"But the east side—that's miles from here. How in the world did you get tied up with them?"

"Really by chance," she explained, "I was visiting the hospital, and the mother was on the maternity ward in a room with one of our members, and we just got to know each other."

"Well, that's fine," the visitation chairman said coldly, "I know we all appreciate your spirit of concern, but what chance do we have of their joining our church from way over there? I mean—if after three months of working on them they haven't made a move . . ."

"Oh, but I haven't tried to get them to join our membership," she replied sweetly. "They attend a little mission church."

"Well, pray tell," he sputtered with exasperation, "what are you doing during all that visitation?"

"I'm just trying to help," she replied cautiously. "I take them used clothing, bits of furniture, a little staple food, and once in a while, provide transportation when it's really needed."

"Now, let's get practical," he continued. "Here for over three months you've been visiting a family that lives on the other side of town, goes to another church, and is in such bad financial shape that if they ever joined they couldn't contribute enough to hold up their end. Now I call that—wasted time and effort."

He stopped to wipe his glasses.

"Now while I'm on this point, let me ask you, Mr. Caveheart, about this jail service our men have every Sunday afternoon."

"Yes, Sir," the old man crowed excitedly. "We're sure proud of that you know—eighteen years and we haven't missed a Sunday."

"I know that, but these men that go with you, how long have they served?"

"Not a man with less than ten years of service," he crowed again. "Great bunch of men—wouldn't miss it for the world."

"Yes, I know," he probed cautiously. "But, again, let's get practical. What good does it do the church? I mean, we're not going to reap many additions, that's for sure."

"Well, that's not the point," the old man sputtered indignantly. "We've had that service for years!"

"I know, but . . ."

"And if we'd ever let it go, that bunch from Central Baptist would move right in! They've been after it for years, but we're not about to let them take it over."

"Oh, I didn't realize that," the visitation chairman said with genuine surprise. "Are they really trying to move in?"

"Sure are," the old man trumpeted like a charging warrior. "We've fought them off for years."

"Well, I certainly didn't know—"

"Let me tell you something else while I'm at it," the old man kept charging. "I don't know why you're so confounded worried about additions from that meeting. This is one bunch we don't want to push for membership. Can you imagine what would happen to our church if a mob of ex-cons started coming to the services?"

"I see your point, yes," the visitation chairman reflected.

"Now don't get me wrong, maybe we could get more results

if we went after some prospects; but this is bigger than all of us. It's a matter of pride, and I know our Lord understands our convictions on this matter."

"Okay, we'll let it ride for now."

The old man sat back, perfectly satisfied that his witness for his Lord had survived another onslaught.

It was at this low point in the meeting that the door flew open. The latecomer was Ted—a real hardnosed "get them for Jesus" witness.

Excitement rippled through the assembled group. Ted had never failed to inspire them with some account of a marvelous conversion.

"The reason I'm late is because I've just come from the hospital." His voice suddenly became very grave.

"I stood by the bed of a child in very critical condition."

The tension was building.

"And in that very room, just a few minutes ago, I led that child's mamma and daddy to Jesus—right there by that bed."

"Praise the Lord," a woman shouted.

"I think you all know the couple," he continued dramatically. "The Barrens family. That young couple that moved into our community about six months ago. You know how we prayed about them and worked on them, and nothing happened."

All heads nodded.

"But, God is faithful," he quickly heralded. "I heard that their child had been taken to the hospital seriously ill, so I ran right over. In fact, I left a very important business deal just sitting on my desk and dashed over there with a prayer on my lips."

"Such dedication," one sighed. "Oh, I wish I had it."

"I got to that couple and told them as comfortingly as I knew how that Jesus was trying to talk to them—that he was trying to reach them through the sickness of their only child."

"Yes, yes," several voices echoed.

"That's when I really let them have it," he sang out, slapping his Bible vigorously.

"I told them as honestly as I knew and with as much love as I could muster that if they wanted that child to survive, they better give their hearts to Jesus."

"Way to go," a voice encouraged him on.

"Man, you have never seen such a moment. It took just a nudge, and they were kneeling by the bed of that child crying their hearts out."

"How's the child doing?" one dared ask.

"Oh, I don't know," he replied, "I really didn't get a chance to ask; I wanted to rush over and share this with you all."

It was a glorious moment for them all. All were reveling in it. The visitation chairman choked a little as he thought:

"It's going to be something like this in glory when we all stand before our Lord. We will hear his precious voice thanking us for all we've done for him. I can hear him now: 'Welcome, welcome, welcome.' "

A Look At the Sheep

Matt. 25:31–40

He still couldn't believe it. Maybe it was a dream, or just his imagination, but he could swear that he heard a voice in the middle of the night saying:

"John, God is coming to visit you at work today—be ready."

He knew it was impossible—or was it? God would actually come to visit him? He couldn't get it out of his head. Over and over, while shaving, while eating breakfast, while driving to work—he kept hearing that voice:

"John, God is coming to visit you today—be ready."

He was still trying to make sense of it as he inserted his key into the lock to open his shoe store.

"I wonder," he thought, "would God actually make himself visible to a common human being?"

Time and time again he tried to shake the sound of that voice that came to him, but he still couldn't seem to get away from its incessant tones:

"Today, John. Today you will get a visit from God."

He barely got the store ready for business when he heard the front door open. His heart leaped within him as he turned.

"Could it be?" he thought to himself excitedly. "But no. Just a woman and a little boy."

"Mr. Stanley?" the woman whispered quietly.

"Yes? What can I do for you?"

"Well, we hate to ask you, but the church at the corner said that you might be able to help my son get a pair of shoes."

He looked at the small boy. His heart went out to him as he saw the tattered sneakers. He smiled at the mother, tenderness sweeping across his face.

"Sure, I can help you," he said pleasantly. "Come here, Son, and let's see what size shoe we need to fix you up with."

This wasn't the first time John had given away a pair of shoes. In fact, he couldn't remember all the times.

"But, so what?" he thought happily. "I'll make a few dollars less, but who wants to see a lad running around in this country without a pair of shoes to protect his feet?"

He finished measuring the little boy, slipped off to the stockroom, and soon returned with a sturdy pair of brown wing tips. He couldn't help thinking as he was slipping the shoes on:

"I wonder if God would really show up and visit me? I just can't believe it."

He shook his head and again realized where he was. He tightened the last lace—slapped the shoe.

"There you are, little man," he said cheerfully. "Wear them in good health."

The mother started to thank him.

"That's all right," he interrupted. "I remember the days when I was a boy that young. Nothing like a new pair of shoes to make you feel like somebody important."

She smiled at him for the first time.

He rubbed the boy's shaggy hair. "God bless you, fellow."

He couldn't help but feel especially good as he watched them leave through the front door.

■ ■ ■

It was late morning when the shadowy figure appeared at the front door. John was standing at the back of the shop and, at first, couldn't make him out.

Again, for a second time that day, his heart leaped within him—"Could it be?"

He squinted at the figure. The light streaming in at the front door blinded him. It was only a moment before the figure stood before him.

John was stunned at first. God he had expected, but this sight he hadn't. The man was filthy. His clothes were almost in shreds. Dry spittle clung to his shrub of a beard.

The man stood there for a long moment staring at John and then spoke.

"I'm hungry."

John didn't ask any questions. He called to his clerk.

"Bob, hold it down around here. I'll be gone for a little while."

John walked over to the cash register and took out some cash.

"Come on," he said gently to the man, "let's get something to eat."

John couldn't help wondering as he walked with the disheveled man to the corner restaurant:

"Suppose God should show up at my shop while I'm gone."

Then, he shrugged. "I must be out of my mind. I'm really starting to believe that dream, or whatever it was."

He spent a long while with the man and found out a lot about him. In fact, he gave the man some suggestions about available work and, as a last gesture, stuffed the remainder of the cash into the man's pocket. The man started to thank him.

"Forget it," John cut in. "God's been so good to me that I really don't mind sharing it."

■ ■ ■

When John finally returned to the shop, it was late afternoon. Just out of curiosity, he asked his clerk:

"Bob, did we have any strange customers?"

"Strange customers, Boss?" the clerk smiled. "What do you mean by that?"

"Oh, nothing, Bob," John replied, smiling to himself. "Forget it. Just something going through my head."

Closing time was nearing now, and John couldn't help but reflect on that voice. It had sounded so certain—so definite:

"God is coming today, John."

The rest of that afternoon dragged on, and finally John decided to call it quits. He told Bob to go on home and started closing down the shop.

As he worked he couldn't help but feel a tinge of disappointment.

"I really didn't expect anything as dramatic as God making an appearance," he muttered to himself, "but it was nice to think that maybe I had been invited to witness a modern miracle."

During those closing moments John was startled by a loud commotion outside his shop. Running to the front door, he found an aged man leaning against his display window coughing violently. He thought the old man might have a heart attack, his body heaved so viciously against the glass.

John ran out to the man and helped him inside to a chair. He wet a small towel and wiped the man's forehead and wrists. In a few moments the old man had quieted down and was breathing normally again.

"I'm glad to see you're feeling better," John said, sighing with relief.

"Thank you," he gasped. "I get those spells every once in a while."

"Is there anything else I can do?" John asked with concern. "I mean, is there anything I can get you—any medicine? There's a drugstore just down the block."

"No, no, I'm all right now," the old man whispered weakly. "Just let me sit for a moment."

John looked at the old man with a certain mellowness welling up in him. The old man reminded him of his father.

"I'd like to drop you off at your home if you wouldn't mind," John said quietly.

"I don't want to put you out any on my account."

"No, no trouble at all. I was just getting ready to close the shop. It will be a pleasure to give you a lift."

After escorting the old man home, John had a few minutes to reflect on the day. He couldn't help but smile to himself as he thought again about that strange voice.

"Oh well," he concluded, "it was a beautiful thought."

■ ■ ■

It was late that night when John was startled awake by a voice—that same voice that spoke to him the night before.

"John, John," the voice began gently.

John found himself actually responding in his stupor.

"Yes? What is it?" he whispered.

John couldn't help but notice his wife sleeping beside him.

"What would she say," he thought, "if she should wake up and find me talking to myself?"

"John, John," the voice came again, this time clearer.

John still couldn't believe it was happening. He shook himself, but he knew he was awake.

"Yes? What is it?" he replied a second time.

"John, it was good to have been with you today—very good indeed."

"With me!" he answered in a startled whisper. "What do you mean—with me?"

"John, I told you I was coming to visit."

"Yes, I know," he sputtered with confusion, "but I didn't see you today. All day long I looked, and I expected, but, God, I didn't see you."

"I was there, John," the voice echoed, "I was there."

"Where, Lord? Where were you?" John continued with wonder. "When did you come?"

"John, John, three times I came—three times, John."

"But I didn't see you, I didn't see you."

John was crying out into the darkness now.

"Yes, you did, John. You not only saw me, but you touched me."

John was completely dazed now.

"John," the voice continued lovingly, "I was the child without shoes."

John's mind whirled back to the little boy.

"And I was the hungry man you fed."

"My Lord," John couldn't help but cry out, "I didn't know."

"And I was the old man you cared for."

It was too much for John to understand.

"But, Lord, those were people—just people," he stammered. "I did care for them, Lord, yes, I did—and I did help them, but I helped them for your sake, Lord."

"No, John, you didn't perform those acts of love and kindness *for* me—but *to* me."

"To you, Lord?" John whispered.

"Yes, John—to me. Inasmuch as you have done it to the least of these that I love—the outcast, the lonely, the needy, the rejected—John, you have done it to me."

John couldn't believe his ears.

"God himself—and today I touched Him!"

"Well done my good and faithful follower," the voice continued, now beginning to fade. "I will look forward to that day when we can meet face to face."

It was at that moment that John's wife awoke. She found John sitting upright in the bed, sweat pouring from his face but a strange look of peace in his eyes.

"John," she whispered with concern, "what's the matter?"

"Nothing, Honey, nothing." He smiled now for the first time. "But in the morning I'm going to tell you a most amazing story."

For Further Reading

CARGILL, ROBERT L. *All the Parables of Jesus.* Nashville: Broadman Press, 1970.

HUNTER, ARCHIBALD M. *Interpreting the Parables.* Philadelphia: Westminster Press, 1961.

JEREMIAS, JOACHIM. *Rediscovering the Parables.* New York: Scribner, 1969.